The Word Witch

WITH LOVE FROM
GREAT UNCLE VIV
IN
AUSTRALIA
CHRISTMAS 2017

The Word Witch

Margaret Mahy

Edited by Tessa Duder ○ Illustrated by David Elliot

HarperCollinsPublishers

Happy reading, Elsie!
Write a poem of your own someday soon!

HarperCollins*Publishers*

First published in 2009
This edition published in 2012
by HarperCollins*Publishers (New Zealand) Limited*
PO Box 1, Shortland Street, Auckland 1140

HarperCollins*Publishers*
31 View Road, Glenfield, Auckland 0627, New Zealand
Level 13, 201 Elizabeth Street, Sydney, NSW 2000, Australia
A 53, Sector 57, Noida, UP, India
77–85 Fulham Palace Road, London W6 8JB, United Kingdom
2 Bloor Street East, 20th floor, Toronto, Ontario M4W 1A8, Canada
10 East 53rd Street, New York, NY 10022, USA

National Library of New Zealand Cataloguing-in-Publication Data

Mahy, Margaret.
The word witch / Margaret Mahy ; edited by Tessa Duder ;
illustrated by David Elliot.
Originally published: 2009.
ISBN 978-1-77554-001-4
1. Children's poetry, New Zealand. [1. New Zealand poetry.]
I. Duder, Tessa. 2. Elliot, David, 1952- III. Title
NZ821.2—dc 23

ISBN: 978 1 77554 001 4

Cover image by David Elliot
Cover and internal typesetting by IslandBridge
Colour reproduction by Graphic Print Group, South Australia

Printed by RR Donnelley, China, on 128gsm Matt Art

Contents

Introduction

The credit for suggesting this collection of Margaret Mahy's poetry belongs to one of her very oldest librarian friends, Elspeth Tindal, who contacted me soon after the publication of my 2005 book *Margaret Mahy: A writer's life*. She wrote of her pleasure at the many memories the book had unlocked, adding, 'I do hope you can persuade someone that Margaret's collected poems would be a good thing . . .'

Of course! How had no one ever thought of this before? Margaret's New Zealand publisher HarperCollins needed no persuading, agreeing with me that the ideal illustrator would be David Elliot — and whose contribution deserves the warmest thanks.

And now — as if Margaret's delicious words on paper and David's whimsical illustrations were not enough — with this new paperback edition can be included Margaret sharing some of her most famous 'party pieces'.

Thanks to her long-time friend and film producer Yvonne Mackay, who spent several days with a crew at Governors Bay, here is recorded Margaret's unique voice giving us 'Down the Back of the Chair' and 'Bubble Trouble' — these and other comic poems heard over the years in countless classrooms, writers' festivals, teachers' and librarians' gatherings. With eyes twinkling, that astonishing and faultless memory and a natural performer's perfect timing, she always brought the house down.

And so to the 66 poems in this collection. We cannot claim this as the definitive 'collected poems', embracing all the verse Margaret ever wrote over five decades. From this most prolific and generous of writers, more, in time, may come to light.

But meanwhile, *The Word Witch* gathers up all her known verse from school readers, collections, picture books, anthologies, magazines and the private papers I was privileged to access in 2004.

Some has been pure happenstance. I was among the audience at the opening of a Christchurch writers' festival when Margaret delivered a brilliant spoof of a Gilbert and Sullivan patter song at breakneck speed. Imagine my delight, finding the original manuscript among her papers many years later.

Then, among those same papers, was the typescript of this book's final poem, 'When I am Old and Wrinkled Like a Raisin', a gentle coda to one of her first ever formal speeches, published in 1973 but long forgotten. What joy to bring this wise and beautiful poem, written when she was only 37, back into the light.

We are all indebted to Celia Dunlop, both for getting Margaret's permission to publish six schoolgirl poems in the *Listener* in 1991, and for her interview with Margaret's English teacher Ian McLean. He told of his student's precocious hunger for literature, classical music, the Savoy operas; we glimpsed Margaret's early understanding of her literary heritage.

This collection shows the full range of her true, mature genius with language. The lyric poems shimmer with imaginative power; the comic verse sparkles with verbal pyrotechnics, all mischief, energy and wit, always technically accomplished. The out-loud reader constantly relishes the bouncing rhythmic patterns, the effortless internal rhymes, the sheer invent-iveness — who else would rhyme 'a string of pearls' with 'a lion with curls'?

The last word lies with Margaret, a rhyming couplet from her Gilbert and Sullivan-inspired festival verses, her 'poetry ethic' in a nutshell:

Free verse is never quite as free as something
with a rhyme to it,
If you're the sort of poet who'll devote a lot of
time to it.

Tessa Duder
Auckland
May 2012

Oh, There was an Old Woman

Oh, there was an old woman
who lived on her own
In a little house made from a smooth
white bone.
And she sat at her door with a
barrel of beer,
And a bright gold ring in her old
brown ear.
And folk who passed by her
they always agreed,
That's a queer little,
wry little,
fierce little,
spry little,
Utterly strange little
woman indeed.

A Witch Poem

The witch my sister from over the sea
Wonderful presents has sent to me.
A whistle to blow and a bell to ring,
Silver ropes for a shining swing,
A golden lion that will play and purr,
Dancing slippers of silver fur,
And, sharp as a needle, bright as a pin,
A mouse that plays on the violin.

Harry the Hawk

Harry the Hawk on his magic trapeze
Flies over the roofs of the city with ease.
He hangs by his heels and he swings by his knees.
Tumultuous Harry the Hawk.

He has the grand acrobatical style.
Stop when you see him and watch for a while.
He has a secret tucked into his smile.
Mysterious Harry the Hawk.

If he should fall, there's no need for dismay,
He'll just give a laugh that is gallant and gay.
Spreading his wings, he'll go floating away.
That's why he's Harry the Hawk.

Bird boy with never a fret or a care,
Woven of sunshine and warm summer air,
Sparrows and stars in the net of his hair.
FANTASTICAL Harry the Hawk.

The Cat Song

We always know just where we're at
Travelling by trusty cat.
Petrol troubles are all gone,
Milk is what we travel on.
On we speed, though once or twice
We have to stop to take on mice.
Goodbye to every mileage sorrow.
Cats! The transport of tomorrow.

The Haunted Child

Oh, I am haunted at my play,
And haunted in my bed,
But does the spirit haunt the house
Or does it haunt my head?

It mutters often in my ear . . .
I know when it's about,
But is it whispering to get in
Or weeping to get out?

The outside rooms, these painted walls
Where I am washed and fed
Are nothing but the shadows cast
By rooms inside my head.

And in the house behind my eyes
I watch the world go by
Strong as a king until I hear
That thin and needling cry.

All shadows, shades and wicked imps,
All creatures of the gloom,
And pucks and pixies may appear
Haunting my outside room.

But oh, but oh, my inside rooms!
Let no ghosts wander there,
And Silence be the only guest
Between my chin and hair.

When I was but a Little Boy

When I was but a little boy and played beneath a tree,
Seven Kings and Seven Queens there came to talk with me.
Their hair was blue as lightning beneath their crowns of gold,
Their faces all were fair and young — their shining eyes were old.

One wore the moon upon his breast, another wore the sun,
The others wore the frosty stars that frozen courses run.

They talked of wise and wondrous things that made my spirits sing.
They made a garland from the winds and crowned me as a king.

They took my hand and ran with me and all grew hushed and still.
The rivers dwindled as we passed. We strode from hill to hill.

The world became a grain of sand washed in a mighty sea,
And Time became a withered leaf blown from its parent tree.

A Summery Saturday Morning

We take the dogs down the wiggly track,
The wiggly track, the wiggly track.
One dog's white and the other dog's black
On a summery Saturday morning.

Bad dogs, bad dogs chase the cat,
Chase the cat, chase the cat.
One dog's thin and the other dog's fat
On a summery Saturday morning.

They chase the boy on the rattly bike,
The rattly bike, the rattly bike.
Chasing things is what dogs like
On a summery Saturday morning.

Long grass grows on the edge of the sea,
The edge of the sea, the edge of the sea.
The wind is blowing wild and free
On a summery Saturday morning.

A goose looks out of the tangled green,
The tangled green, the tangled green.
Her neck is long and her eye is mean
On a summery Saturday morning.

Another goose . . . and then another,
Then another, then another!
Seven sleek sisters out with mother
On a summery Saturday morning.

The geese begin to run away,
Run away, run away.
The dogs run, too. They want to play
On a summery Saturday morning.

We run, too, to catch the dogs,
To catch the dogs, to catch the dogs —
Scattering shells and leaping logs
On a summery Saturday morning.

The mud begins its guggliwugs,
Its guggliwugs, its guggliwugs.
Our sandals slide like slugliwugs
On a summery Saturday morning.

The geese turn round and flap and hiss,
Flap and hiss, flap and hiss.
The dogs were not expecting this
On a summery Saturday morning.

The geese begin to chase us back,
To chase us back, to chase us back.
Out of the mud and up the track
On a summery Saturday morning.

If you want to walk in peace,
Walk in peace, walk in peace,
Don't let your dogs upset the geese
On a summery Saturday morning.

The Pines

Hear the rumble,
Oh, hear the crash.
The great trees tumble
The strong boughs smash.

Men with saws
Are cutting the pines —
That marched like soldiers
In straight green lines.

Seventy years
Have made them tall.
It takes ten minutes
To make them fall.

And, breaking free
With never a care,
The pine cones leap
Through the clear, bright air.

17 Kings and 42 Elephants

Seventeen kings and forty-two elephants
Going on a journey through a wild wet night,
Baggy ears like big umbrellaphants,
Little eyes a-gleaming in the jungle light.

Seventeen kings saw white-toothed crocodiles
Romping in the river where the reeds grow tall,
Green-eyed dragons, rough as rockodiles,
Lying in the mud where the small crabs crawl.

Forty-two elephants — oh, what a lot of 'ums,
Big feet beating in the wet wood shade,
Proud and ponderous hippopotomums
Danced to the music that the marchers made.

Seventeen kings sang loud and happily,
Forty-two elephants swayed to the song.
Tigers at the riverside drinking lappily,
Knew the kings were happy as they marched along.

Who joined the singsong? Cranes and pelicans,
Peacocks fluttering their fine fantails,
Flamingos chanting 'Ding Dong Bellicans!'
Rosy as a garden in the garden vales.

Tinkling tunesters, twangling trillicans,
Butterflied and fluttered by the great green trees.
Big baboonsters, black gorillacans
Swinging from the branches by their hairy knees.

Kings in crimson, crowns all crystalline,
Moving to the music of a single gong.
Watchers in the jungle, moist and mistalline,
Bibble-bubble-babbled to the bing-bang-bong!

Seventeen kings — the heavy night swallowed them,
Raindrops glistened on the elephants' backs.
Nobody stopped them, nobody followed them —
The deep dark jungle has devoured their tracks.

The Snail

Your snail — he carries his house on his back,
And his house has never a door,
And when he goes, he goes but slow
And his horns go on before.

Welcoming Song

Dance upon silver, dance upon gold,
We have a baby, one day old.

Dance on a peacock, dance on a pearl,
The baby's a sister, because it's a girl.

Dance upon velvet, dance upon silk,
It sleeps in its cradle and dreams about milk.

Dance upon butterflies, dance upon bells,
Its little curled hands are like little pink shells.

'Its name?' the wind asks in a whispery tongue.
But its name is a secret too dear to be sung.

Dining Out

Out in the darkness —
Harry and me —

Having a fork-and-fingers
Tea.
Potatoes boiled
In an old black pot,
And eggs for supper —
That's what we've got.

Smouldery red,
The planet Mars
Mirrors our fire
Among the stars,
And sparks leap into
The gentle night
Like baby comets ablaze
With light.
The trees and the grass
Draw close to see —
Out in the darkness,
Harry and me.

When the King Rides By

Oh what a fuss when the king rides by —
And the drum plays *rat-a-plan-plan!*

Oh what a fuss when the king rides by —
The puss-cat runs and the pigeons fly
And the drum plays *rat-a-plan-plan!*

Oh what a fuss when the king rides by —
The dogs all bark and the babies cry,
The puss-cat runs and the pigeons fly,
And the drum plays *rat-a-plan-plan!*

Oh what a fuss when the king rides by —
The soldiers stamp and the ladies sigh,
The dogs all bark and the babies cry,
The puss-cat runs and the pigeons fly,
And the drum goes *rat-a-plan-plan!*

Oh what a fuss when the king rides by —
The people throw their hats up high,
The soldiers stamp and the ladies sigh,
The dogs all bark and the babies cry,
The puss-cat runs and the pigeons fly,
And the drum goes *rat-a-plan-plan!*

Oh what a fuss when the king rides by —
Mice in their mouse-holes wonder why,
The people throw their hats up high,
The soldiers stamp and the ladies sigh,
The dogs all bark and the babies cry,
The puss-cat runs and the pigeons fly,
And the drum goes *rat-a-plan-plan!*

Oh what a fuss when the king rides by —
Rockets dance in the starry sky,
Mice in their mouse-holes wonder why,
The people throw their hats up high,
The soldiers stamp and the ladies sigh,
The dogs all bark and the babies cry,
The puss-cat runs and the pigeons fly,
And the drum goes *rat-a-plan-plan!*

Circles

Two loaves of bread are very well,
One to eat and one to sell.
With the money that I get
I buy a bird to be my pet.

Eating bread like any king
I hear the bird begin to sing.
Catch the song without delay —
Quick, before it flies away.

Getting paper, pen and ink,
Sit and dream and sit and think.
Quickly catch in net of words
Taste of bread and song of birds.

Take the poem I have made
(Quite a long one, I'm afraid),
Rush to clever printing man,
Sell the poem if I can.

Ring the merry money bell!
(Doesn't money jingle well?)
Bored with money, buy instead
Two good loaves of crusty bread.

Two loaves of bread are very well
One to eat and one to sell.
One to sell and buy — who knows —
A silver fish or flowering rose.

Puck's Song

I'm in love with the wind, and the sky, and the sea;
I am part of the earth, and the earth's part of me.
I love the green hills that for ages gone by
Have stood with their crests in the blue of the sky.

I belong to the hills, and the marsh, and the fen,
And the purple-black shadows that play in the glen;
Mine are the breezes that dance o'er the lea;
I am part of the earth, and the earth's part of me.

Mine is the sweep of the hills in the sun,
Mine are the dusks when the daylight is done,
Mine are the clouds and the sunlight so fair;
Mine the cool stars and the crystal-clear air.

Sunrise and sunset, darkness and light,
Breath of the morning and voice of the night —
Nought in the earth is a secret from me,
Who am one with the air, and the earth, and the sea.

Magic

Is there no magic in the world?
Is sun just sunshine, raindrops rain?
Are they not fairy gold and pearls?
Is not the wind a fairy train?

Is all the world of magic gone?
Are there no roadways through the grass,
Which mice draw matchbox coaches on,
Along which fairy workmen pass?

Is all the world of magic gone?
Are not the roses fairy homes?
Is not the earth beneath our feet
Alive with goblins, elves and gnomes?

If all the world of magic's gone,
And witches do not sail the sea
In egg-shells halved, with broom-stick oars —
This world is not the place for me.

The Remarkable Cake

It's Christmas — the time when we gather to make
A truly remarkable once-a-year cake.
The recipe's written in letters of gold
By a family witch who is terribly old.

The rule of this cake is it has to be made
In a wheelbarrow (stirred with a shovel or spade)
At Christmas, the season of love and good will.
Other times of the year it might make you feel ill.

You must nail it together or stitch it with glue,
Then hammer it flat with the heel of your shoe.
You must stretch it out thin, you must tie it in knots,
Then get out your paint box and paint it with spots.

What a taste! What a flavour! It's certain to please,
It's rather like ice cream with pickles and cheese.
In June it would taste like spaghetti and mud,
While its taste in September would curdle your blood.

Oh, what a cake! It looks simply delicious.
Now get out the carving knife, get out the dishes!
Be careful! Be careful! This cake might explode,
And blow up the kitchen and part of the road.

At the sudden cry of trouble, Mother took off at the double,
For the squealing left her reeling . . . made her terrified and tense,
Saw the bubble for a minute, with the baby bobbing in it,
As it bibbled by the letter-box and bobbed across the fence.

In her garden Chrysta Gribble had begun to cry and cavil
At her lazy brother, Greville, reading novels in his bed.
But she bellowed, 'Gracious, Greville!' and she grovelled on the gravel,
When the baby in the bubble bibble-bobbled overhead.

In a garden folly, Tybal, and his jolly mother, Sybil,
Sat and played a game of Scrabble, shouting shrilly as they scored.
But they both began to babble and to scrobble with the Scrabble
As the baby in the bubble bibble-bobbled by the board.

Then crippled Mr Copple and his wife (a crabby couple),
Set out arm in arm to hobble and to squabble down the lane.
But the baby in the bubble turned their hobble to a joggle
And they raced away like rockets . . . and they've never limped again.

Even feeble Mrs Threeble in a muddle with her needle
(Matching pink and purple patches for a pretty patchwork quilt),
When her older sister told her, tossed the quilt across her shoulder,
And she set off at a totter in her tattered tartan kilt.

Now at the shops a busy rabble met to gossip and to gabble,
Started gibbering and goggling as the bubble bobbled by.
Mother, hand in hand with Mabel, flew as fast as she was able,
Full of trouble lest the bubble burst or vanish in the sky.

After them came Greville Gribble in his nightshirt, with his novel
(All about a haunted hovel) held on high above his head,
Followed by his sister, Chrysta (though her boots had made a blister),
Then came Tybal, pulling Sybil, on the Scrabble for a sled.

After them the Copple couple came cavorting at the double,
Then a jogger (quite a slogger) joined the crowd who called and coughed.
Up above the puzzled people — up towards the chapel steeple —
Rose the bubble (with the baby) slowly lifting up aloft.

There was such a flum-a-diddle (Mabel huddled in the middle),
Canon Dapple left the chapel, followed by the chapel choir.
And the treble singer, Abel, threw an apple core at Mabel,
As the baby in the bubble bobbled up a little higher.

Oh, they giggled and they goggled until all their brains were boggled,
As the baby in the bubble rose above the little town.
'With the problem let us grapple,' murmured kindly Canon Dapple,
'And the problem we must grapple with is bringing baby down.'

'Now, let Mabel stand on Abel, who could stand in turn on Tybal,
Who could stand on Greville Gribble, who could stand upon the wall,
While the people from the shop'll stand to catch them if they topple,
Then perhaps they'll reach the bubble, saving baby from a fall.'

But Abel, though a treble, was a rascal and a rebel,
Fond of getting into trouble when he didn't have to sing.
Pushing quickly through the people, Abel climbed the chapel steeple
With nefarious intentions and a pebble in his sling!

Abel quietly aimed the pebble past the steeple of the chapel,
At the baby in the bubble wibble-wobbling way up there.
And the pebble *burst* the bubble! So the future seemed to fizzle
For the baby boy who grizzled as he tumbled through the air.

What a moment for a mother as her infant plunged above her!
There were groans and gasps and gargles from the horror-stricken crowd.
Sybil said, 'Upon my honour, that's a baby who's a goner!'
And Chrysta hissed with emphasis, 'It shouldn't be allowed!'

But Mabel, Tybal, Greville, and the jogger (christened Neville)
Didn't quiver, didn't quaver, didn't drivel, shrivel, wilt.
But as one they made a swivel, and with action (firm but civil),
They divested Mrs Threeble of her pretty patchwork quilt.

Oh, what calculated catchwork! Baby bounced into the patchwork,
Where his grizzles turned to giggles and to wriggles of delight!
And the people stared dumbfounded, as he bobbled and rebounded,
Till the baby boy was grounded and his mother held him tight.

And the people there still prattle — there is lots of tittle-tattle —
Then the glory in the story, young and old folk, gold and grey,
Of how wicked treble Abel tripled trouble with his pebble,
But how Mabel (and some others) saved her brother and the day.

George's Pet

When George and his gorilla
Go bounding down the street,
They get respectful nods and smiles
From neighbours that they meet.

If George had owned a puppy dog,
Or else a kitty-cat,
His neighbours wouldn't notice him
With courtesy like that.

Gay Wind

A gay wind, merry with autumn,
Comes round the chimney stack
Carrying bright leaf riders
High on its bounding back.

And the chimney standing stiffly,
So brave and black and bold,
Looks like a strong stern soldier
Hung with medals of gold.

And the chimney standing stiffly,
Where mortar and brick have bound him,
Looks like a dark enchanter
With dancers of gold around him.

The Fantail

Green on the hill tops, green in the trees,
Green and silver in the wild bright seas.
But Jane found a place where the sun shone yellow.
Here danced a sharp little black and tan fellow,
Who winked and who prinked on the bough.

Patchwork patterns on the dark leaf-mould,
Nets of shadow held the sun's hot gold,
And he called to the world to be glad, to rejoice,
In a wheel-barrow-squeaking-in-the-garden voice,
As he this-wayed and that-wayed,
He twinked and he prinked on the bough.

Oh, what a dancer!, Oh, what a day!
('Boom' went the breakers in the wet brown bay).
And he danced in a fashion you were glad to see
In a crazy zigzag on a deep green tree.
As he
      High-footed — low-footed,
      This-wayed and that-wayed,
      He twinked and he prinked
On the bough.

The King of Castile

The King of Castile (feeling foolish and old)
Said 'Bring me a cure! I'm catching a cold.'
So a butler in blue brought a bottle of wine,
Saying, 'Do try it, sir! It's remarkably fine.'
It tasted of phoenixes, tasted of flowers,
It tasted of summer-time's happiest hours.
It smelt like a garden, it sang like a song
With the thrill of the flute, and the throb of a gong.

And the King, huddled up in his ivory bed,
Felt it go like a fountain of fire to his head.
In his crown (and pyjamas) he leaped to his feet
And danced, like a dragon-fly, into the street,
Away flew his crown, and it looked, as it rolled,
Like a hedgehog whose bristles were covered in gold.
And people who noticed said . . . 'What an odd thing!
It shows that he isn't just any old king.
It's not very stately, but how very GAY
Of the King of Castile to behave in this way.'

Once upon an Evening

Once upon an evening
    Looking overhead,
I saw the little crescent moon
    Like a silver thread.

Then rocks burst into blossom,
    And horns blew, sweet and shrill,
    And kings and queens in scarlet
Came shining down the hill.

The Burnt Library

Here as they came and all too swiftly went,
The hours of happy solitude I spent;
But for a space I left, and now, returned,
I find my place of silent worship burned.
Here Eliot, Auden, Steinbeck, Lewis, James
Have moved the world, but could not move the flames;
And with them Pope whose shrilly-cutting ire
Has met its master — all-devouring fire.
Mark! Dickens crumbled 'neath the flaming thrust,
And Marlowe's 'mighty line' is in the dust.
Here Shakespeare held his once imperial sway;
Where is his golden thunder then today?
Where are Othello, Hamlet, Lear, Macbeth?
They lie with Shaw in silent ashen death.
And Dante with Defoe and Dekker fell;
No Virgil came to guide him through the Hell;
See how he mingles ashes on the floor
With Homer, Hardy and Sir Thomas More.
And Forster's here; now I shall never know
Where his Celestial Omnibuses go.
See — Shelley's brilliant passion is today
All dull and cold and spent in ashes grey . . .
So shall we be. Wise, foolish, mean and just
Shall sleep together in tomorrow's dust;
The prince and peasant shall appear as one,
As motes of dust seen in a ray of sun.

The Tin Can Band

Oh, the tin can band,
Oh, the tin can band!
It's the dinniest band
In the big bright land.
It's a sing-song band, it's a bing-bong band,
It's a miss-a-beat, have-a-treat, skippy-feet band.
As we march along with our pots and pans,
And we bing and bong on our old tin cans.

We're a-singing and a-songing to the binging and the bonging.
We're escaping and a-skipping out
On every hand.
And it sounds like a battle
When our tin cans rattle,
When our tin cans rattle
And our tin cans clang.
Yes, it's sounding like the prattle and the tattle of a battle
Like a merry monster cannon going BANG, BANG, BANG!

Though silence falls when the band goes by,
And the street is bare to the hills and sky,
There's a nitter and a natter,
And a tiny tinny patter,
Like a whisper (only crisper)
Like a tin toy's sigh,
And a flutter like a mutter,
Like a sunny sort of stutter,
Going giggling down the gutter
Where the funny echoes die.

Out of My Ship between the Stars

Out of my ship between the stars
I stare out into space
A thousand suns and galaxies
Look back into my face.

The suns are bright as trumpet calls,
The moons, like wind bells, chime.
I am the centre of a wheel
That spins in space and time.

Dashing Dog

Dashing dog! Dashing dog! Oh, what a sight to see!
Cleaned up and curlicued! What a delight to be
Greeting a dog that is brushed-up-and-downery,
Devil-dog-daring, and dog-about-townery.

Seen with a dog that is dapper and dandified,
We'll appear glorious, gallant and grandified.
What a dog! What a dog! Fit to inspire us all.
Let us go walking, so folk can admire us all.

Down on the sand gulls perambulate, pondering,
Keeping one eye on whoever goes wandering.
Off goes the dog, keen to catch every quill of them.
Up go the gulls, every feather and bill of them.

Sandy and sticky, and cock-a-hoop capery,
Tangled in seaweed by way of a drapery,
Straggling and salty, and spotted and sandified,
Somehow our dog is no longer so dandified.

Breakers are bounding! The breezes are sighing past.
Out of the sand dunes a Frisbee comes flying past.
Horrors! Our dog has leaped up and is catching it,
Seizing it, scrounging it, stealing it, snatching it.

Three other dogs think our dog has done wrong to them,
Sure that the Frisbee should really belong to them.
All in a moment, our darling is twirled about,
Ruffled and scruffled and wobbled and whirled about.

Never mind! Never mind! He's still respectable.
Some of the damage is quite undetectable.
Brush off that seaweed and make him all orderly,
Then we will stroll along, dreamy and dawdle-y.

Dreamy and dawdle-y? Oh, look at that, my dear!
Snooping through sea grass is somebody's cat, I fear.
Horrors! He's seen it! He's off like a thunderbolt.
Trouble-quick, double-quick, devil-dog-dunderbolt.

Into a briar rose, all rambling and riotous —
Wind whistles! Thistles seem ready to fly at us!
Sea grass and bracken and broom may be bearable.
Dog in a briar rose? The damage is terrible.

Wind on the jetty blows out like a gale to sea,
Where's baby Betty? Oh, how could we fail to see!
We were distracted, our little one bumbled off,
Right down the jetty! And *splash*! She has tumbled off.

Run! How we run! But a comet goes ripping past,
Rushing and racing and speedily skipping past,
Diving and dipping where Betty is floundering,
Saving our girl from the danger of drowndering!

Hurrah for the hero who swims, full of cheer, to us,
Bringing back Betty, so precious and dear to us!
Out on the jetty we're towing, then tugging them,
Petting and patting and holding and hugging them.

Look at him walking there — docile and dutiful,
Dragging and dripping . . . but utterly beautiful
Look at that wagging tail, wet, every bend of it,
But he's our HERO — and that is the end of it.

Hide and Seek in a Dark House

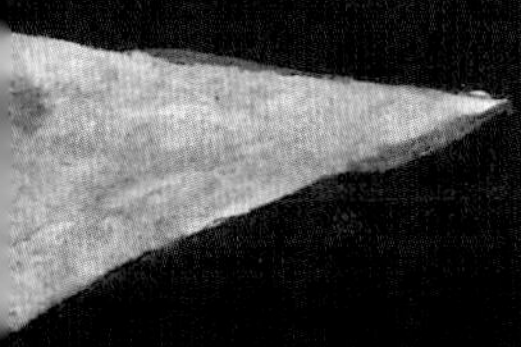

In and out the window
In and out the door!
Up the path and round again,
Sliding on the floor.

Breathing through the keyhole,
Whispering on the stair,
Hiding by the dust bin,
Crouching by the chair!

Now without a candle,
Turning off the light,
We're a rustling circus
Entertaining Night.

We're the circus people,
Acrobat and clown,
Pulling shadows round us
Drawing darkness down.

Only Night can see us
Flitting room to room
Wiped away by blackness
Painted out by gloom.

In and out the darkness
Who can really see?
Are the others changing?
Am I really me?

Wonderful Me

On one side the hills
On the other the sea,
On the beach in the middle
There's wonderful me.

I am made out of sticks
I am made out of salt,
And whatever might happen
It isn't my fault.

I am made out of seaweed
I am made out of stones,
And my heart is a bird
In a cage of white bones.

I am made out of froth
I am made out of foam,
I am spinning the world
So I daren't go home,
Or else like a penny,
Or else like a top,
The world would spin slower
   and slower
   and stop.

On the beach in the middle
There's wonderful me,
And on one side the hills,
On the other the sea.

The Fairy Child

The very hour that I was born
I rode upon the unicorn.
When boys put tadpoles in their jars
I overflowed my tin with stars.
Because I sing to see the sun
The little children point and run.
Because I set the caged birds free
The people close their doors to me.
Goodbye, goodbye, you world of men —
I shall not visit you again.

Clowns

Zing! goes the cymbal, Bang! goes the drum.
See how they tipple-topple-tumbling come,
Dazing the country, dazzling the towns.
Here's the procession of the circus clowns.

Hop on the heel and twist on the toe.
See how they wibble-wobble-waddling go.
Bim-bam-balloons in the clear blue air!
Clowns on the march to they-don't-know-where.

Painted-on smiles that are long and loud
Beam at the giggle-gaggle-goggling crowd.
Under the paint do they grin so gay?
Nobody sees so I just can't say.

Look how the clowns all a-cantering come
Riding their donkeys with a hee-haw-hum.
Where have they come from? Where do they go?
They kin-can't say for they din-don't know.

Bush Wedding

The parson-bird shall marry us,
The bell-bird ring the bell.
The wax-eye shall our witness be
And all will then be well.

The morepork shall provide the feast,
The kiwi bird the key
That opens doors to magic lands
Where you may come with me.

What I Like . . .

What I like for dinner when I'm on my own
Is Fish and Chips, Asparagus tips,
And an ice-cream cone.

What I like for dinner when I have a guest
Is Mossy Fudge, and Muddly Sludge,
And baked Bird's Nest.

Plans Gone Wrong

On the edge of the well sat the wicked king.
He lifted his voice and began to sing:

'However wicked I've been before
I'm going to be wicked again and more.

'A hundred kingdoms shall be mine.
I'll wash their streets with blood and wine.

'A thousand cities shall bow and weep.
Their scrambling people shall die like sheep.

'On the gates of the sky my name shall ring,
And I shall be king, king, king, king, KING!'

That's what the wicked king sang as he sat
Planning the wickedness he would be at.

But he slipped as he sang and he drowned in the well.
You never can tell. You never can tell.

Hiccups

Oh, horrors! Look at Mother! She is slamming down the phone.
Through her lips there comes this mumble and a melancholy moan.
'Oh, what has happened, Mother? You have turned a ghastly grey.
What!!! Granny's in a taxi and she's calling in today!'
Just when Baby's got the hiccups!

Goodness gracious guzzleguts! Oh, gilly-golly-gosh!
Quickly! Hide the dirty dishes that we haven't time to wash.
Brush the cat hair off the cushions! Vacuum up the crusts and crumbs!
Let's be looking trim and tidy by the time our granny comes!
Curses! Baby's got the hiccups.

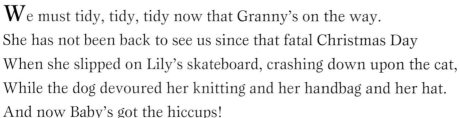

We must tidy, tidy, tidy now that Granny's on the way.
She has not been back to see us since that fatal Christmas Day
When she slipped on Lily's skateboard, crashing down upon the cat,
While the dog devoured her knitting and her handbag and her hat.
And now Baby's got the hiccups!

Oh, bring the children inside. Fetch them in and sponge them down,
For Granny's in a taxi and she's rocketing through town,
And she likes a house that's tidy . . . Wipe those soup stains off the floor!
We must one and all be perfect by the time she's at the door.
But Baby's still got hiccups!

Jack's busy playing football. He is racing for a goal,
When Mum runs in and tackles him. The coach cries, 'Bless my soul!'
He quickly tries to sign her up. He likes her forward play,
But football counts for nothing when your granny's on the way.
And Baby's got the hiccups!

So Jack is washed behind the ears and made to change his shirt,
Though he is not the only one rejoicing in the dirt.
There's Father in the garden looking like a Brussels sprout,
But Mum is quite relentless and she quickly weeds him out.
Listen! Baby still has hiccups.

Now, Lily, run and fetch the twins from underneath the shed.
Oh! They're burrowing like rabbits and they're mud from toe to head.
We must swishy-swishy-swash them. We must rub-a-dub them clean,
Crying, 'Giddy goats and griffins! Granny's racing to the scene!'
And Baby's got the hiccups! What a time to get the hiccups!

We are trembling, we are tidy, we are starched and stuck in place.
We are standing feet together; there is fear on every face.
For our granny is approaching. She is at the corner now
When the dog commences howling, and he wrinkles up his brow.
Oh, how can we stop the hiccups?

Oh, Baby is a darling, but the hiccups . . . What a shame!
If she hiccups at our granny, we are bound to get the blame!
Oh, her hiccups shake the kitchen. It is getting much too much.
She is rattling all the saucepans and the silverware and such.
Such a bad attack of hiccups!

How do you cure the hiccups? 'Give the kid a fright,' cries Jack.
'Once you're frightened, hiccups vanish, and they say they don't come back!'
Let us terrify the baby! Let us roar like crocodiles!
But Baby only hiccups in between her sunny smiles.
For she doesn't *mind* her hiccups.

Let us try a drink of water. That is sure to do the trick.
So Baby drank the water, then she hiccupped and was sick!
So we had to change her feeder, and her cardigan and dress.
And she giggled and she gurgled and she hiccupped through the mess —
The day our Baby had the hiccups.

'We are doomed to harbour hiccups,' Father yells in deep despair.
'It is destiny!' moaned Mother, falling backwards in her chair.
But Baby laughs and hiccups — yes, she hiccups and she grins
At her mother and her father, Jack and Lily, and the twins.
She rather likes her hiccups!

Oh, look! The door is open. There's Gran arrived, at last.
Is she going to forgive us for that fatal Christmas past?
She has bought another handbag. She has bought a brand-new hat,
Which alarms the dog (and Father) and which terrifies the cat!
Just when Baby's got the hiccups!

'Give the child to me!' cries Granny. 'I am old enough to know
That the proper kind of cuddle often makes the hiccups go!
Though your dog once ate my handbag, that's a long way in the past . . .
If the oldest hugs the youngest then the hiccups cannot last.'
Even very stubborn hiccups!

Granny hugs our darling Baby and she kisses Baby's head.
And then Baby stops her hiccups, doing just what Granny said.
'I am getting old,' said Granny. 'I am nearly ninety-three.
So now I've solved the problem, may I have a cup of tea?
And we'll overlook the hiccups!'

Bring her tea and bring her biscuits! Bring a slice of Lily's cake!
Yes, but should we let her eat it? Could it be a bad mistake?
'It's been lovely,' mumbles Granny, 'and we've had a lovely talk.'
Then . . . *hiccup! Hiccup! Hiccup!* rattled every spoon and fork.
Now *Granny* has the hiccups!

Then Lily laughs, and Jack laughs too — the twins laugh even more.
And Mum begins to giggle, whereas Daddy starts to roar!
And Baby grins and gurgles (though her laugh is very small),
While Granny hiccup-hiccuping, laughs loudest of us all.

The Storm King's Daughter

A young man stood by the edge of a stream,
And the Storm King's daughter saw him there,
And down she whirled like a wild witch dream
Wrapped all around in her long black hair.

'Carry me, carry me over the water!'
'Who are you, who are you?'
'I'm the Storm's daughter.
The river rises under my hand
Running in ruin over the land.
Even the ocean, breaking free
From moon-mapped courses, follows me,
While over the hills my father cries
Shaking the summits, bruising the skies.
Around his neck on coppery rings
Are dragons' jewels and crowns of kings.
Carry me, carry me over the water,'
Cried the Storm King's strange and beautiful daughter.

'I'll not carry you over the water
For you can flow from here to there,
Or ride on the wind, or swim like a swan,
Or weave a bridge from your long black hair.'

But the Storm King's daughter took the young man
Twixt finger and thumb like a wheaten grain
And carried him off to her castle of thunder,
Drawing behind her a curtain of rain.

#

(To the tune of 'Our great Mikado, virtuous man',
from *The Mikado* by Gilbert and Sullivan.)

Our great headmaster, virtuous man,
When he to rule our school began,
Resolved to try
A plan whereby
His pupils might be steadied;

So he declared in accents sweet
That eating ice-cream in the street
Should not be done by folks discreet
Who feared his stern detention;
For as all folks of sense will see,
The street is not the place for tea.
And he was right, alas, alright,
And he was right as right can be.
This new and devastating rule
Caused great dismay throughout the school;
Third formers new,
And prefects too,
Were equally affected.
The ice-cream merchant eyed his ware,
And bit his nails and tore his hair,
For, tho' with hungry eyes they'd stare,
The pupils dare not enter.
And you'll allow, as I expect,
That this would have a sad effect
Upon the careless and correct
Of Whakatane children.
And he was right, etc.
Exam time once again is here.
The teachers shake their heads: 'Dear, dear,
'This average — Oh!
'It's very low;
'Why, ten's the highest rating.'
That ice-cream rule has played the deuce,
For ice-cream is a lot of use
In sharp'ning up the mind obtuse;
Ice-cream is stimulating.
And yet with all we must agree
That he was right to so decree,
And he was right, etc.

Uncle James

My Uncle James
Was a terrible man.
He cooked his wife
In the frying pan.

'She's far too tender
To bake or boil!'
He cooked her up
In peanut oil.

But sometime later —
A month or more —
There came a knock
On my uncle's door.

A great green devil
Was standing there.
He caught my uncle
By the hair.

'Are you the uncle
That cooked his wife,
And leads such a terribly
Wicked life?'

My uncle yowled
Like an old tom cat,
But the devil took him,
For all of that.

Oh, take a tip
From my Uncle James!
Don't throw stones
And don't call names.

Just be as good
As ever you can —
And never cook aunts
In a frying pan!

For the Opening of Books and Beyond

(To the tune of 'I am the very model of a modern Major-General',
from *The Pirates of Penzance* by Gilbert and Sullivan.)

I have written many poems but I think this is the best of all,
A dithyrambic ditty to extol our city festival;
A dithyramb, for those who lack a vocab academical,
Is a Dionysian choric hymn, poetic not polemical.
And though some philistines may cry 'No! Bugger all! It's doggerel,'
All connoisseurs of poetry will gape and be a-goggeral.
Free verse is never quite as free as something with a rhyme to it,
If you're the sort of poet who'll devote a lot of time to it.
As form competes with chaos the explosions can be various,
Revealing Art as heavenly, hypnotic or hilarious.
Wake, wake then, Art! Bestow on us your blessings bright and aureate,
According to instructions from the local poet laureate.

As wintertime approaches other cities start to aestivate,
But in the Garden City we wake up and start to festivate.
The season which in other towns breeds angst and deep anxiety,
Fills everyone in Christchurch with a longing for variety.
Ignoring indications of hibernal frigidity,
The city opens up to art with cordial avidity,
Theatres, squares and galleries display our great diversity,
A balcony or bus stop can become a university;
A festival's explosive — there are some who think it facile,
But it's frolicking — it's rollicking, aesthetic razzle-dazzle.
And if there's any one thing over which the town can glory at
It's being told to 'Go it!' by a local poet laureate.

We go lurching, ever searching for the moment that translates us all,
The word, the note, the image that so strangely recreates us all . . .
We look for dissolution, the true instant of dumbfoundedness
When Art conspires to face us and reveal its true unboundedness.
We flow into the universe and cosmic magic fills us all,
Our petty agitations cease as contemplation stills us all;
Though I'm the sort of laureate who tends to make a joke of it,
We've artists who exemplify the glory, pain and yoke of it.
It's like a wand transfiguring the long, the short and tall of us,
It's like a firework going off, illuminating all of us,
A truly thrilling flare-up is the underlying quest of all,
Go out! Rise up like rockets! And enjoy the city festival.

The Reluctant Hero,
or
Barefoot in the Snow

When he put on his socks in the morning
He found they were much too tight.
His feet, without any warning,
Had lengthened over night.
He didn't have any others,
He couldn't pick or choose.
He borrowed a pair of his mother's
And went to put on his shoes.

When he put on his shoes in the morning
He found they were much too tight.
His feet, without any warning,
Had lengthened over night.
His toes and heels were skinned — oh,
His feet had grown like roots.
His shoes went out of the window
And he went to put on his boots.

When he put on his boots in the morning
He found they were much too tight.
His feet, without any warning,
Had lengthened over night.
His little toe was just in,
He had to squash and squeeze.
He threw them into the dust bin
And he went to put on his skis.

When he put on his skis in the morning
He found they were much too tight.
His feet, without any warning,
Had lengthened over night.
He had no footware which in
His feet could feel at ease.
The skis went into the kitchen
And his toes were left to freeze.

And so he went out barefoot,
No socks or shoes he wore.
He trod in places where foot
Had never trod before.
And everywhere his feet sent
A message to the sky.
His footprints down the street meant
A hero's passing by.

Unexpected Summer Soup

I drank some soup this afternoon,
And what do you think I found in my spoon?
    Onions and Peas!
Of course I didn't mind.
It's what you'd expect to find.

I drank some soup this afternoon,
And what do you think I found in my spoon?
    Onions and Peas,
        A Hive of Bees . . .
Oh, what a surprise!
I couldn't believe my eyes.

I drank some soup this afternoon,
And what do you think I found in my spoon?
    Onions and Peas,
    A Hive of Bees,
    A Crown, A Carrot . . .
Oh, shivers and shocks!
I nearly jumped out of my socks!

I drank some soup this afternoon,
And what do you think I found in my spoon?
    Onions and Peas,
    A Hive of Bees,
    A Crown, a Carrot,
    A Patchwork Parrot . . .
A-ghast, a-gape, a-gog,
I nearly stood on the dog!

I drank some soup this afternoon,
And what do you think I found in my spoon?
　　Onions and Peas,
　　A Hive of Bees,
　　A Crown, a Carrot,
　　A Patchwork Parrot,
　　A Sprig of Sage . . .
I didn't choose to object,
It's what you might expect.

I drank some soup this afternoon,
And what do you think I found in my spoon?
　　Onions and Peas,
　　A Hive of Bees,
　　A Crown, a Carrot,
　　A Patchwork Parrot,
　　A Sprig of Sage,
　　A Frog in a Cage . . .
What do you say to that?
It certainly scared the cat.

I drank some soup this afternoon,
And what do you think I found in my spoon?
　　Onions and Peas,
　　A Hive of Bees,
　　A Crown, a Carrot,
　　A Patchwork Parrot,
　　A Sprig of Sage,
　　A Frog in a Cage,
　　A Witch's Shoe . . .
Taken unaware,
I tumbled off my chair.

I drank some soup this afternoon,
And what do you think I found in my spoon?
	Onions and Peas,
	A Hive of Bees,
	A Crown, a Carrot,
	A Patchwork Parrot,
	A Sprig of Sage,
	A Frog in a Cage,
	A Witch's Shoe,
	And a Mermaid too
Who sang a song so sweet and shrill
That the summery day outside stood still.

I asked my mother where she sat,
'How do you make a soup like that?'
'You have to gather, you have to guard,
Things odd and even, striped and starred,
All the dark things, all the light,
That come to your door by day or night,
It isn't easy at all, my dear,
But I'll make it again another year,
With . . .
	Onions and Peas,
	A Hive of Bees,
	A Crown, a Carrot,
	A Patchwork Parrot,
	A Sprig of Sage,
	A Frog in a Cage,
	A Witch's Shoe,
	And a Mermaid too . . .
A Song, a Story, and anything more
That a summer wind brings to my door.'

How the World Ended

'If you don't believe in fairy tales
The world will break in half,'
Said the little boy,
And that made all the big boys laugh.

'We believe in whales and sails,
Water in pails,
Snails,
Running noddy-topped quails,
Towels hanging from rails,
Jails,
The sting of ice when it hails,
The banging-in of nails,
Chasing our dogs over hills and dales,
And catching them by their wigging wagging whipping tails,
But none of us believes in Fairy Tales.'

Then . . . the moon went out
    and the sun rushed about,
And the world fell in half like a tired old thing
And out came a WITCH on the end of a spring
Proving the world was a magical Jack-in-the-box,
Full of Red Riding Hood, Cinderella, Clever Hans, the
Musicians of Bremen and Reynard the Fox,
And mermaids, clowns, kings, magicians and Jolly Tars.

All these fell out of the middle of the world
And tumbled, singing, outwards towards the stars,
Which they blew out like candles on a birthday cake,
And that was the end of everything — even television and porridge . . .
. . . didn't those big boys make a mistake?

The Star-crossed Lovers

'Oh, do you remember, my darling . . . ?'
'I cannot remember,' said he,
'But was I a succulent starling
When you were the leaf on a tree?

'And then I turned into a trumpet
And you were the music I played.
And was I a hot buttered crumpet
When you were some fresh marmalade?

'I know I have met with you often
But cannot remember the place.
I was once an astrologer's coffin
And you were the smile on his face.

'We're acquainted but never together,
We encounter but never unite.
For I was a spell of bad weather
When you were a Saturday night.

'Are we dice that the devil is tossing?
Are we never permitted to choose?
I was once a pedestrian crossing
When you were a pair of old shoes.

'Both bound by a singular star, still
Our places in space don't agree,
For I am a conjuror's castle
And you are a cake for his tea.'

Christmas in New Zealand

Our Christmas Day is blue and gold,
And warm our Christmas night.
Blue for the colour of Mary's cloak
Soft in the candle-light.
Gold for the glow of the Christmas Star
That shone serene and bright.
Warm for the love of the little babe
Safe in the oxen stall.
We know our Christmas by these signs
And yet around my wall
On Christmas cards the holly gleams
And snow flakes coldly fall,
And robins I have never seen
Pipe out a Christmas call.

Sensible Questions

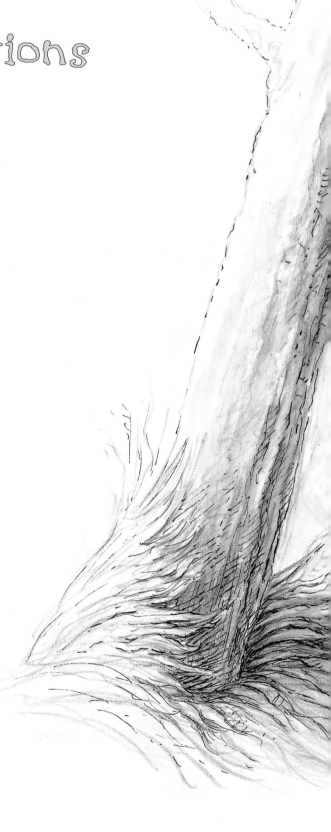

'Suppose the land turned into the sea?'
'Don't be stupid! It couldn't be!'

'Suppose the sea turned into the land?'
'It wouldn't happen. You don't understand!'

'Suppose I waved this grassy stalk,
And Max the dog began to talk?'

'Your fancy's foolish. Your ways are wild!
I often think you're a silly child!'

But Marigold waved her stalk of grass
And all she had asked about came to pass.

The land rolled up and the sea rolled over
The waves were covered with grass and clover,

While Marigold and her reproving aunt
Who'd kept on saying 'Don't!' and 'Can't!',

Were up to their necks in a wild green sea —
And Max the dog said: 'Fiddle dee dee!'

The Ghastly Nightmare,
or
The Butcher's Dream

Our butcher dreamed the other night
That, spry as any elf,
Each leg of mutton took a crutch
And went off by itself,

That all the little sausages
Grew tails and furry feet,
And, sliding from their butcher's hooks,
They ran into the street.

And suddenly the shop was filled,
As far as he could tell,
With people wanting mutton legs
And sausages as well.

Sea Song

This is my place, my very own place,
Staring the ocean straight in the face.

Every morning I wake to find
The ocean in front and the hills behind.

Every morning I wake to see
The ocean carefully watching me.

I watch the ocean back again.
It stamps and whinnies and tosses its mane.

Bright and dangerous, bold and free,
Only a fool would trust the sea.

Mighty waters that call and move,
Only a fool could help but love.

Standing here I can know the sea,
But what in the world does it make of me?

Dreaming, dancing, false and true,
I can be bright and dangerous too.

Holding the hills and the sea and the sky,
A little reflection drowned in my eye.

Prefabricated

The school was growing larger — the fit was rather tight,
The teachers used to grumble, the pupils used to fight.
To the Auckland Education Board this letter was dictated:
'Please send to Whakatane two new rooms (prefabricated).
'The colour doesn't matter — at first we thought a pink —
'But navy blue is better, as it doesn't show the ink.
'The roof must match the walls, of course; again — well navy blue.
'But this is incidental. We will leave the rest to you.'
The Auckland Education Board's reply was really pleasant:
'Afraid we haven't got a stick of navy blue at present,
'So we're sending you a cyclamen with window panes of cream.
'And we hope that you will find it quite a pleasing colour scheme.'
Two lorries brought them to the door and swiftly went away.
The Head with joy unpacked them. They were both a pretty grey:
And tied with purple ribbon was a card for all to see:
'A prefabricated present from the Education B.'

Baby is Falling Asleep

The happy home rumbles with racket and rumpus
and Mother and Father both jiggle and jump as
the fracas flows in from each point of the compass . . .
yet baby is falling asleep.

Kate's in the kitchen. She's grousing and grumbling
at Sam on his skates. He is sliding and stumbling
upsetting the saucepans. Ka-BOOM! They go tumbling!
But baby is falling asleep.

Florrie and Fern are commencing a flounce-about!
Two of the cats start a passionate pounce-about,
dogs begin barking, embroiled in a bounce-about.
Baby is drifting to sleep.

Mervyn makes music no ceiling can soften. He
blows on his bagpipes. Amazing how often he
hits a wrong note, and produces cacophony!
Baby has fallen asleep.

Sleep, little darling, through family clattering,
blaring and banging and booming and battering,
pinging and popping and piping and pattering!
Sink into whispering sleep!

The Tarragon Vinegar Song

Only the best and the finest ingredients
Do for a song that is written for you,
Ravenous uncles and many thin greedy aunts
Yearn for the music so lively and new.
'What did you put in this song?' they all say,
'To make it turn out this exotical way?'

Tarragon, tarragon, tarragon vinegar,
Bubble-cake-custard and blueberry ice,
Butterfly bacon and cutlet of crocodile,
Make up a mixture worth double the price.

Kings and their courtiers come to investigate,
Queens in kimonos consistently call,
Presidents knock on the east or the westi-gate,
Princes on ponies jump over the wall.
'Oh, are you a man from the echoless moon
That you play this fantastamalogical tune?'

Tarragon, tarragon, tarragon vinegar,
Willow leaves, whiskers and waterfall wine,
Potpourri pancakes and cream of the dandelion,
Make up a melody friendly and fine.

For they all love the music — relations and royalty,
Lawyer and layabout, doctor and nurse.
A thief tried to steal it. His plans were all spoilt. He
'S now just a line in the very last verse.
He is trapped by the words, but he constantly hears
The harmonious hum of heavenly spheres.

Tarragon, tarragon, tarragon vinegar,
Oceans are heard in the heart of a shell.
Hippos and harlequins join in a harmony
Kings in their crowns cannot conquer or quell.

Alone in the House

Who? Who? Who was that whispered?
Who was it spoke in a magical tongue?
Did some white witch pass under my window?
Was that a thread of the song she sung?

Dark, dark, dark grow the shadows.
Is that the rattling of goblin drums?
Alone in the house with the cat and the mouse,
And, no-body, no-body comes.

King of the World

Right on the edge of the night, and the edge of the town,
Where the houses and daylight ended, where the grass and the stars began,
A funny old bundle of ragged clothes
Turned out to be a man.

He was just sitting there, gently brown,
Like an autumn leaf, tattered and curled.
I said 'Hello!' and 'Who are you?' and he said,
'I'm the King of the World.'

'Only don't tell anyone,' (he said), 'because I'm tired of it all.
The crown I had to wear was my father's and it didn't fit me.
It was made of gold, but it slid down over my eyes,
And I couldn't see.'

'It made faces look all squashed out sideways.
Fancy looking at squashed out faces all day!
I got tired of the desert I lived in, all velvet and diamond dust,
So I ran away.'

'Don't tell anyone I'm King of the World . . .
Let it be our secret — yours and mine.'
And he turned his old brown face to the evening sky,
And drank up the wind like wine.

The Flingamango

Oh the wily flingamango
Is a very agile bird
He can dance a pretty tango
Though his foxtrot is absurd.

In a ballet dress of paper
He will whirl for half the night
Sending those who see him caper,
Into Transports of Delight!

The Springing Granny

The winter with ice on the edge of its teeth
Blew snow in the sandpit and hail on the heath.
And, sliding through keyholes and any odd cracks,
Ran shivery fingers down everyone's backs.

'Enough!' cried the granny of Sally and Fred.
'I'm getting my comics and going to bed.
Outside there is nothing but struggle and storm
And my bed is so comfy and cosy and warm.'

So they put her to bed, downy pillows around her.
The winter wind couldn't get near her to hound her.
Said Granny, 'The winter is really a strain,
And I'm not getting out of bed ever again.'

'I'm worn out and wrinkly and wispy and white,
And nobody takes me out dancing at night.
My spring is all gone, and I grumble and groan!
I'll invent a new spring that's completely my own.'

So she painted her sunshade a beautiful blue,
With a big yellow sun and a white cloud or two.
And she fixed it all up so it covered her bed —
A spangle of springtime spread over her head.

Then, dreaming of sunshine and sea on the beach
And bananas in bunches that hung within reach,
She quickly constructed a couple of palms,
Using tattered umbrellas with sticky-out arms.

Next, she painted some butterflies, fixed them on wires,
And sent her old coverlet out to the dyers.
They patched up the place held together with string
And dyed it as green as a meadow in spring.

Reclining at ease on her meadowy quilt,
Granny covered the places where soup had been spilt
By embroidering buttercups, crocuses, clover,
Until the quilt burgeoned and blossomed all over.

Then she sighed and lay back, feeling very contented,
Enjoying the strange sort of spring she'd invented —
A primrose-and-pineapple *tropical* spring
Of the kind that would cause any granny to sing.

Every day after lunch (in her satin pyjamas),
She dreamed (as she snored) of the sunny Bahamas
Where curling waves lazily broke on the shore,
And pythons and parrots looked in at her door.

It was all right for Granny . . . but Sally and Fred
Were kept on the run between kitchen and bed.
'Oh, Sally — take Granny her cake and her tea,
And please rub the liniment into her knee!

And Fred — go to Granny and take her a hotty.
Here's one for her feet — oh, and one for her botty!
Take Granny the paper. Be quiet when you play!'
It was up-and-down, up-and-down all of the day.

Granny read all of her comics, ate nuts by the score
(While carelessly dropping the shells on the floor).
'Oh, Fred, sweep them up! Here's a dustpan and brush . . .
But remember she's sleeping! For goodness' sake, *hush.*'

Said Sally, 'I'm fed up to *here* with this fuss!
There just has to be something in it for us.'
'We could trundle her out to the park,' muttered Fred.
'There are people who'd *pay* to see Granny in bed.'

So the next day, when Granny was having a nap,
(With nutshells and comic books spread in her lap),
Her tropical springtime in boisterous bloom,
Fred and Sally together crept into her room.

They were silent as shadows; they worked with a will
Guiding Granny (and bed) with remarkable skill
Out over the landing, then on down the stairs,
Round the hall table and hatstand and chairs.

Out over the gap where an old step had gone . . .
They bumped a few times but their Granny slept on,
Entranced by a dream in which pineapple-ices
Were served on a seashore all scented with spices.

And she dreamed that her singing had made her a star —
She had glittery boots, an electric guitar!
Like a rocket at midnight she lit up the dark . . .
Then she woke with a fright: *she was out in the park!*

And all round her bed, from her head to her feet,
Were the neighbours who lived in the wintertime street —
All clapping their hands and beginning to sing
Their rapturous praises of Granny and spring . . .

A spring to be looked at, and longed for and felt,
A springtime so real that the snow had to melt,
While the sky, which for weeks had been lowering and grey,
Was tender and blue as the clouds rolled away.

She was suddenly famous! A tourist so keen,
Was making a video of the whole scene,
While TV directors with cameras and crews
Were clustered around shooting scenes for the news.

'Hey, Fred!' muttered Gran. 'Make the most of this chance,
If you charge them all extra this granny will dance.
Go get me a helping of fried fish and chips,
And I'll dance a fandango and turn a few flips.'

'I slept through the winter, but now I'll get up.
For I'm feeling as fresh and as fit as a pup.
The world is so full of remarkable things,
It is spring in my bed . . . and my bed's full of springs.'

'I'll spring till the spring springs. When springtime is sprung,
I'll still keep on springing although I'm not young.
And I'll prove to the folk who come flocking to see
That there's nothing but spring in a granny like me.'

So she sprang and she sprang, springing higher and higher,
She sprang like a lark, or a flame of the fire . . .
And winter retreated, the morning turned pearly,
And springtime arrived a full week or two early.

My Sister

My sister's remarkably light,
She can float to a fabulous height.
It's a troublesome thing,
But we tie her with string,
And we use her instead of a kite.

Further Adventures of Humpty Dumpty

Humpty Dumpty, King of the Eggs,
Ran down the road on his little short legs.
After him, quickly, came forty-two cooks
Who lived in a castle of cookery books,
Charging and barging the length of the street,
Holding their egg beaters ready to beat,
Shouting out 'Omelettes!' and 'Scrambled!' as well.
What a terrible shock for a king in a shell!

Ghosts

Two ghosts are walking out today,
And one I cannot see:
The ghost of what I was before,
And what I am to be.

The ghost of what I was before
Is still a friend to me;
The other ghost — the one I fear —
Is what I am to be.

If I could draw the veil aside,
Perhaps then I could see
The face of this, the stranger ghost,
The one I am to be.

Yet I am blessed in this, I feel:
The future's hid from me,
And I must wait to meet the ghost
Of what I am to be.

There are two ghosts abroad today —
And one I cannot see:
The first, a wraith of what I was,
The other is to be.

The Silly Song

Hey ding a ding,
Hey ding a dong,
Life is so silly,
And so is this song.

A telegraph pole is immensely absurd.
It stands on one leg like a sort of bird.
It stands on one leg and pretends it's not there,
While workers on ladders are plaiting its hair.

Hey ding a ding,
Hey ding a dong,
Life is so silly,
And so is this song.

The very tall houses they're building these days
Have their toes in the town and their heads in a haze.
You go up in a lift and incredibly soon
You can knock on the door of the man in the moon.

Hey ding a ding,
Hey ding a dong,
Life is so silly,
And so is this song.

There's nothing as mad as the cars in the street.
They trundle on wheels where they ought to have feet.
But if they had feet they would only get corns
And then they'd start grumbling and blowing their horns.

Hey ding a ding,
Hey ding a dong,
Life is so silly,
And so is this song.

The telegraph poles and the houses and cars
May sing the same song that is sung by the stars,
But if ever I start such a wonderful song
It always comes out as a Hey ding-a dong.

Hey ding a ding,
Hey ding a dong,
Life is so silly,
And so is this song.

The Man from the Land of Fandango

The man from the land of Fandango
Is coming to pay you a call.
With his tricolour jacket and polka-dot tie
And his calico trousers as blue as the sky
And his hat with a tassel and all.
And he bingles and bangles and bounces,
He's a bird! He's a bell! He's a ball!
The man from the land of Fandango
Is coming to pay you a call.

Oh, whenever they dance in Fandango,
    The bears and the bison join in,
And baboons with bassoons make a musical sound,
    And the kangaroos come with a hop and a bound,
And the dinosaurs join in the din,
    And they tingle and tongle and tangle
Till tomorrow turns into today.
    Then they stop for a break and a drink and a cake
In their friendly fandandical way.

The man from the land of Fandango
    Is given to dancing and dreams,
He comes in at the door like a somersault star
    And he juggles with junkets and jam in a jar
And custards and caramel creams.
    And he jingles and jongles and jangles
As he dances on ceilings and walls,
    And he only appears every five hundred years
So you'd better be home when he calls.

The Witch
and
the Scarecrow

Out in the fields of tossing grass
A scarecrow saw a witch go past.
Her hair was pale as thistledown
Her tall hat had a pointed crown.

Her face was full of magic wild
She was a witch's magic child
And, softly, as she went along
She sang a strange enchanted song.

The scarecrow could not say a word
Of what he'd seen and what he'd heard,
He stood all day the corn amid
And kept the witch's secret hid.

A Strange Old Man

I shan't forget if I live to be
Even as old as a hundred and three,
The strange old man that I happened to pass
Curled like a snail in the sweet green grass.

By his pointed knee was an old grey cat,
And magpies three on his shoulder sat,
And COBWEBS covered his mouth and eyes —
Oh, what a horrible horrid surprise!

And I somehow knew that that strange old man
Had been sitting there since the world began,
Had been sitting there while winds and rains
Beat mountain tops into grassy plains,

Had been there while dancing seas and lands
Changed their places and clapped their hands.
And that old man will be sitting about
When the world runs down and the stars go out.

Down the Back of the Chair

Our car is slow to start and go.
We can't afford a new one.
Now, if you please, Dad's lost the keys.
We're facing rack and ruin.
No car, no work! No work, no pay!
We're getting poorer day by day.
No wonder Dad is turning grey.
The morning is a blue one.

Nothing but dockets in his pockets,
raging with despair,
Dad acts appalled! Though nearly bald,
he tries to tear his hair.
But Mary, who is barely two,
says, 'Dad should do what I would do!
I lose a lot, but I find a few —
down the back of the chair.'

Well, he's patted himself, and searched the shelf.
He's hunted here and there,
so now he'll kneel and try to feel
right down the back of the chair.
Oh, it seemed to grin as his hand went in.
He felt it tingling under his skin.
What will a troubled father win
from down the back of the chair?

152

Some hairy string and a diamond ring
were down the back of the chair.
Pineapple peel and a conger eel
were down the back of the chair.
A sip, a sup, a sop, a song,
a spider seven inches long.
No wonder that it smells so strong —
down the back of the chair.

A packet of pins and one of the twins,
were down the back of the chair.
A pan, a fan that belonged to Gran,
down the back of the chair . . .
A crumb, a comb, a clown, a cap,
a pirate with a treasure map,
a dragon trying to take a nap —
down the back of the chair.

A cake, a drake, a smiling snake,
were down the back of the chair.
A string of pearls, a lion with curls,
down the back of the chair.
A skink, a skunk, a skate, a ski,
a couple of elephants drinking tea,
a bandicoot and a bumblebee,
down the back of the chair.

But what is this? Oh, bliss! Oh, bliss!
Down the back of the chair.
The long lost will of Uncle Bill,
down the back of the chair.
His money box all crammed with cash,
tangled up in a scarlet sash.
There's treasure, pleasure, toys and trash —
down the back of the chair.

'I've found our dreams,' our father beams,
'down the back of the chair.
At last I see how life can be,
down the back of the chair.
Forget the keys! We're poor no more.
Just call a taxi to the door.'
A taxi shot out with a roar
from down the back of the chair.

The chair, the chair, the challenging chair,
the champion chair, the cheerful chair,
the charming chair, the children's chair,
the chopped and chipped but chosen chair.
To think our fortune rested there —
down the back of the chair!

Goodness Gracious!

Goodness gracious, fiddle dee dee!
Somebody's grandmother out at sea!

Just where the breakers begin to bound
Somebody's grandmother bobbing around.

Up on the shore the people shout,
'Give us a hand and we'll pull you out!'

'No!' says the granny. 'I'm right as rain,
And I'm going to go on till I get to Spain.'

The Dictionary Bird

Through my house in sunny weather
Flies the Dictionary Bird,
Clear to see on every feather
Is some outlandish word.

'Hugger Mugger' 'gimcrack' 'guava'
'Waggish' 'mizzle' 'swashing rain'
Bird — fly back into my kitchen,
Let me read those words again.

Hush! Hush! Hush!

'Hush! Hush! Hush!' sings the wind on the hill.
'Hush, you rackety world. Hold still!'
The ocean sings as it strokes the land.
'Shush!' sigh the waves on the soft, sea sand.
'Hush!' says the moon looking out of the night.
'Hush to my darling, my heart's delight.'

When I am Old and Wrinkled Like a Raisin

When I am old and wrinkled like a raisin
I will dance like a kite on the bucking back of the wind.
I won't look ahead at the few bright days I am facing
Or look back at the years trailing out like streamers behind.

Everyone else will be gone. The silence will seem to be mocking,
But I will dangle and dance in the bright clear air of the day
Kicking my old stick legs in their red striped stockings.
An old leaf wrinkled and brown but golden and gay.

Dance, dance, little old feet. Spin on your halfpenny of time.
Roar, little old lion, in your meadow of cobwebs and rust
Till you burn with the fiery power of the dance and the rhyme
And fall back to the earth in a sprinkle of golden dust.

Acknowledgements

The publishers are grateful to the people and publishers concerned for their permission to reprint the poems in this collection.

17 Kings and 42 Elephants, between publishers

A Strange Old Man, Learning Media

A Summery Saturday Morning, Penguin UK

A Witch Poem, Learning Media

Alone in the House, Orion

Baby is Falling Asleep, HarperCollins New Zealand

Bubble Trouble, Frances Lincoln Ltd

Bush Wedding, Orion

Christmas in New Zealand, Learning Media

Circles, Orion

Clowns, Learning Media

Dashing Dog, HarperCollins Australia/ Margaret Mahy

Dining Out, Orion

Down the Back of the Chair, Frances Lincoln Ltd

For the Opening of Books and Beyond, Margaret Mahy

Further Adventures of Humpty Dumpty, Learning Media

Gay Wind, Orion

George's Pet, Orion

Ghosts, New Zealand Listener

Goodness Gracious!, Orion

Harry the Hawk, Orion

Hiccups, Margaret Mahy

Hide and Seek in a Dark House, Orion

How the World Ended, Learning Media

Hush! Hush! Hush!, HarperCollins New Zealand

King of the World, Learning Media

Magic, New Zealand Listener

My Sister, Orion

Oh, There was an Old Woman (from the story 'Mrs Bartelmy's Pet' from *The Second Margaret Mahy Story Book*), Orion

Once upon an Evening, Learning Media

Out of My Ship between the Stars (from the story 'The Curiosity Concert'), Orion

Plans Gone Wrong, Learning Media

Prefabricated, New Zealand Listener

Puck's Song, New Zealand Listener

Sea Song, Orion

Sensible Questions, Orion

Song, New Zealand Listener

The Burnt Library, New Zealand Listener

The Cat Song, Margaret Mahy

The Dictionary Bird, Orion

The Fairy Child, Orion

The Fantail, Orion

The Flingamango, Orion

The Ghastly Nightmare, or *The Butcher's Dream*, Learning Media

The Haunted Child, Orion

The King of Castile, Orion

The Man from the Land of Fandango, Orion

The Pines, Orion

The Reluctant Hero, or *Barefoot in the Snow*, Orion

The Remarkable Cake, Orion

The Silly Song, Orion

The Snail, Learning Media

The Springing Granny, Margaret Mahy/ Watson, Little Ltd (licensing agents)

The Star-crossed Lovers, Orion

The Storm King's Daughter, Orion

The Tarragon Vinegar Song, Orion

The Tin Can Band, Orion

The Witch and the Scarecrow (from the story 'The Curiosity Concert'), Orion

Uncle James, Orion

Unexpected Summer Soup, Orion

Welcoming Song, Orion

What I Like . . ., Orion

When I am Old and Wrinkled Like a Raisin, Margaret Mahy

When I was but a Little Boy, Orion

When the King Rides By, Learning Media

Wonderful Me, Learning Media

About . . .

the poet

Margaret Mahy

Margaret Mahy is one of the world's best-loved authors, writing wonderfully funny and imaginative children's poems, stories and picture books as well as ground-breaking novels for young adults, thrilling millions of readers for over forty years.

A member of the Order of New Zealand, an Honorary Doctor of Letters and twice winner of Britain's Carnegie Medal for Children's Literature, she has also been honoured by the Arts Foundation of New Zealand as a Living Icon, received the Prime Minister's Award for Literary Achievement in Fiction, and been awarded the Hans Christian Andersen Medal for her outstanding contribution to children's literature.

Margaret lives in Governors Bay, New Zealand, and has two daughters and seven grandchildren.

the editor

Tessa Duder

Tessa Duder has published more than 35 books — novels, picture books, non-fiction, plays and anthologies for children; a collection of short stories, anthologies and non-fiction for adults. Her lifelong admiration for Margaret Mahy was reflected in her portrait *Margaret Mahy: A writer's life*, published in 2005.

Among her awards are six prizes for her acclaimed *Alex Quartet*, as well as the Margaret Mahy Medal and an OBE for her contribution to children's literature. She has also been awarded fellowships to spend time in France and Antarctica, and in 2008 an honorary doctorate from the University of Waikato.

Currently working on a young adult novel, Tessa lives in Auckland, New Zealand. She has four daughters and two grandchildren.

Visit her website at www.tessaduder.com.

the artist

David Elliot

David Elliot is an award-winning children's illustrator and author. He has written and illustrated five picture books of his own, including the *Sydney Penguin* books and *Pigtails the Pirate* (winner of the 2003 New Zealand Post Children's Picture Book Award). He has also illustrated for many other New Zealand children's authors, including Jack Lasenby, Janet Frame, Joy Cowley and Pauline Cartwright. *The Word Witch* is his first book for Margaret Mahy.

Since 2002, David has been illustrating internationally for Brian Jacques' *Redwall* and *Castaways* series and also for US authors T.A. Barron and Jeffrey Kluger.

David lives in Port Chalmers, New Zealand, with his wife and two teenage daughters.

His work can be viewed online at www.davidelliot.org.

FAST VEGETARIAN FOOD

50 fresh, tasty
recipes made
in minutes

FAST VEGETARIAN FOOD

Matthew Drennan
Photography by Amanda Heywood

southwater

To Mark and my parents, Jim and Betty, with thanks.

This edition is published by Southwater

Southwater is an imprint of
Anness Publishing Limited
Hermes House
88–89 Blackfriars Road
London SE1 8HA
tel. 020 7401 2077
fax 020 7633 9499

Distributed in the UK by
The Manning Partnership
251–253 London Road East
Batheaston
Bath BA1 7RL
tel. 01225 852 727
fax 01225 852 852

Published in the USA by
Anness Publishing Inc.
27 West 20th Street
Suite 504
New York
NY 10011
fax 212 807 6813

Distributed in Australia by
Sandstone Publishing
Unit 1
360 Norton Street
Leichhardt
New South Wales 2040
tel. 02 9560 7888
fax 02 9560 7488

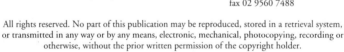

© 1996, 2001 Anness Publishing Limited

1 3 5 7 9 10 8 6 4 2

Publisher: Joanna Lorenz
Senior Cookery Editor: Linda Fraser
In-house Editor: Jillian Stewart
Designer: Alan Marshall
Photographer: Amanda Heywood
Home Economist: Stephen Wheeler
assisted by Lucy McKelvie

For all recipes, quantities are given in both metric and imperial
measures, and, where appropriate, measures are also given in standard
cups and spoons. Follow one set, but not a mixture, because they are
not interchangeable.

Previously published as *Step-by-Step: 15-Minute Vegetarian*

CONTENTS

INTRODUCTION

Vegetarian food has finally become a major part of our cuisine. We no longer need to justify the inclusion of vegetarian dishes on restaurant menus, and a cookery book such as this is to be universally celebrated and not seen as catering to the few. The notion that vegetarian dishes are uninspired, heavy and dull has long been dispelled, but one myth that does persist is the idea that vegetarian food is fussy and time-consuming. Fast food has become an important part of our culture. The demand for "real food" in this area is increasing, and vegetarian food is no exception.

Step-by-Step 15-Minute Vegetarian proves how easy it can be to produce a delicious vegetarian lunch or dinner in less time than it takes to reheat a ready-made meal from the supermarket. The emphasis is on freshly prepared produce cleverly coupled with staples from store cupboard or freezer.

The secret of success when speed is essential is to make sure you have all the ingredients and necessary equipment before you begin. Advice on stocking the store cupboard and what constitutes a survival kitchen is given on the next few pages. For quick cooking, cut ingredients to a similar size and remember that root vegetables will take longer than most greens. Master the "all hands on deck" method, using the time while one item is cooking to prepare the next, and you may be surprised to discover just how swift a cook you can be.

So whether you are a committed vegetarian, enjoy the occasional vegetarian meal, or just want something simple and satisfying because you are in a hurry or too tired to spend long in the kitchen, this book brings you the means of making fantastic home-cooked meals in moments.

The Store Cupboard

Your store cupboard should be the backbone of your kitchen. Stock it sensibly and you'll always have the wherewithal to make a tasty, satisfying meal. Begin with the basics and expand as you experiment, buying small quantities where possible and keeping an eye on "use by" dates.

OILS, SAUCES AND CANNED GOODS

Chilli oil
Use this fiery oil sparingly to liven up vegetable stir-fries and similar dishes.

Groundnut oil
This bland-tasting oil will not mask delicate flavours. It is good for deep-frying. Use vegetable or sunflower oil instead, if you prefer.

Olive oil
If you must have only one oil, a good olive oil will suit most purposes (except deep-frying). Extra virgin olive oil is more expensive and best kept for salads.

Sesame oil
Favoured in oriental cooking for its flavour, this rich oil can be used on its own or combined with vegetable oil.

Ghee
This is pure clarified butter. Used extensively in Indian cooking, it is usually sold in blocks or cans.

Black bean sauce
A thick aromatic sauce made from beans, used for marinades and stir-fries.

Passata
This thick sauce is made from sieved tomatoes. It is mainly used in Italian cookery.

Soy sauce
A thin, salty, black liquid made from fermented soya beans. Add a splash at the end of cooking and offer extra at the table.

Sun-dried tomatoes
These deliciously sweet tomatoes, baked in the sun and dried, are sold in bags or in jars, steeped in olive oil.

Tahini paste
Made from ground sesame seeds, this paste is used in Middle Eastern cookery.

Tomato purée
This is a concentrated tomato paste which is sold in cans, jars or tubes. A version made from sun-dried tomatoes is also now available.

Canned pulses
Chick-peas, cannellini beans, green lentils, haricot beans and red kidney beans survive the canning process well. Wash in cold running water and drain well before use.

Canned vegetables
Although fresh vegetables are best for most cooking, some canned products are very useful. Artichoke hearts have a mild sweet flavour and are great for adding to stir-fries, salads, risottos or pizzas. Pimientos are canned whole red peppers, seeded and peeled. Use them for stews and soups, but stick to fresh peppers for anything else as they lack the firmness of bite that is needed for dishes such as stir-fries. Canned tomatoes are an essential ingredient to have in the store cupboard. There is now a very wide range available, whole or chopped, plain or with herbs, spices or other flavourings. Additional useful items to include are ratatouille (make sure it is a good brand, though) and sweetcorn.

chick-peas

tahini paste

tomato purée

golden syrup

red wine

chilli sauce

chopped
tomatoes

chilli
oil

herb vinegar

pimientos

sweetcorn

black olive
paste

white wine
vinegar

ratatouille

black bean
sauce

kidney beans

lentils

soy sauce

chillies in oil

tahini
paste

plum tomatoes

olive
oil

mustard

honey

passata

groundnut
oil

red wine
vinegar

balsamic
vinegar

salad dressing

ghee

Dry Goods

Assuming your store cupboard already includes flours, sugars and dried fruits, the following items are invaluable for speedy cooking. The list of spices relates specifically to the recipes contained in this book.

Bulgur wheat
This whole wheat grain is steam-dried and cracked before sale, so only needs a brief soaking before use. Keep it cool and dry in the cupboard and it will last for a few months.

Nuts
Buy nuts in small quantities and store in a dry place. Almonds, cashews, peanuts, pecans, pine nuts and walnuts all feature prominently in this book.

Pasta
While fresh pasta is generally preferred, both for flavour and for speed of cooking, the dried product is a very valuable store cupboard ingredient. Spaghetti, noodles (Italian and oriental) and shapes are all useful.

Rice
If you stock only one type of rice, make it basmati, which has a superior flavour and fragrance. A mixture of basmati and wild rice (not a true rice, but the seeds of an aquatic grass) works well.

SPICES

Caraway seeds
Small greenish-brown seeds with a nutty texture and a flavour reminiscent of aniseed or fennel.

Chinese five-spice powder
Made from a mixture of anise pepper, cassia, fennel seed, star anise and cloves, this spice has an enticing aniseed (licorice) flavour.

Garam masala
This is an aromatic mixture of different spices used widely in Indian dishes. It is usually added at the end of cooking.

Ground cardamom
Fragrant, with a spicy undertone, cardamom is used in sweet and savoury dishes.

Ground cinnamon
A sweet fragrant spice ground from the dried rolled inner bark of a tropical tree.

Ground coriander
With a warm savoury aroma, this spice imparts a mildly hot yet sweetish flavour.

Ground cumin
Sweet and pungent, with a unique and distinctive taste.

Ground turmeric
With a somewhat musty flavour and aroma, this spice adds a deep yellow colour to food. It is sometimes used in place of saffron to add colour, although it does not have the same flavour.

Saffron
This is the most expensive spice in the world. It has a pungent scent with a slightly bitter-sweet taste. The threads are crushed and steeped in a little liquid before use.

rice

ground turmeric

ground cumin

caraway seeds

egg noodles

nuts

penne

*bulgur
wheat*

pecan nuts

*garam
masala*

dried chillies

spaghetti

cornflour

mixed spice

*black
peppercorns*

*Chinese five-
spice powder*

pine nuts

poppy seeds

*chilli
powder*

*ground
coriander*

sea salt

thyme

cumin seed

caster sugar

*long grain
rice*

*granulated
sugar*

garlic

Fresh Produce

Beautifully fresh herbs and vegetables from around the world are readily available in our supermarkets. This vegetable checklist highlights both familiar and less well-known items.

HERBS

Basil
Well known for its affinity with tomatoes, basil has a rich spicy aroma.

Coriander
A pungent, slightly sweet herb, commonly used in Indian cooking.

Oregano
This herb has a strong flavour. It is widely used in Italian cooking.

VEGETABLES

Aubergine
A glossy oval or round vegetable, usually purple, aubergine is delicious grilled, fried or stuffed.

Chillies, red or green
Members of the capsicum (pepper) family, these are small and can be very fiery. Take care when handling chillies not to touch your eyes and mouth, as chillies contain an irritant which can sting sensitive skin.

Fennel
A bulbous leaf stalk with a distinct aniseed flavour. Fennel can be eaten raw in salads, or cooked.

Shallots
These small bulbs have a mild onion flavour and are ideal for using in sauces.

Shiitake mushrooms
An oriental mushroom with a fairly meaty scent and flavour. The stems are quite tough and are best discarded.

Cheeses and Tofu

Improvements in handling and distribution mean that we are now able to buy a huge range of local and imported cheeses in excellent condition. Tofu, available in various forms, is another valuable source of protein.

Blue cheese
Where a recipe fails to specify a particular blue cheese, use Roquefort if a strong flavour is required and dolcelatte for a milder result.

Camembert
This cheese is made from cow's milk. It has a mild creamy taste with a slight acidic edge that gets milder with age.

Feta
This soft Greek cheese is rindless, white in colour and has a crumbly texture. It is slightly sour, piquant and quite salty to the taste.

Goat's cheese
Fresh goat's cheese is soft and creamy. As it ages, the cheese becomes harder and the flavour intensifies.

Mozzarella
A unique Italian cheese made from cow's milk, mozzarella has a mild, creamy taste and an unusual spongy texture.

Parmesan
A hard cheese from Italy with a wonderful, distinctive flavour. It is usually grated or shaved wafer-thin. Buy it fresh as the ready-grated cheese sold commercially often lacks flavour.

Stilton
An English semi-hard cheese with blue veins, Stilton has a soft moist texture and a strong flavour.

Tofu
This is an unfermented bean curd made from soya beans. It absorbs flavours readily and is frequently marinated before use. Various forms are available, from soft silken tofu to a firm type which can be cubed and sautéed.

goat's cheese

feta

dolcelatte

Stilton

mozzarella

Parmesan

Camembert

Equipment

Stocking up on every item in your local cookware shop will not make you a better cook, but some basic items are definitely worth investing in.

A few good saucepans in various sizes and with tight-fitting lids are a must. Heavy-based and non-stick pans are best. A large non-stick frying pan is invaluable for the quick cook. The food cooks faster when spread over a wider surface area. For the same reason, a good wok is essential. I suggest using a large saucepan or frying pan when the recipe calls for occasional stirring, and a wok for continuous movement, such as stir-frying.

Good quality knives can halve your preparation time, but more importantly, a really sharp knife is safer than a blunt one. You can do yourself a lot of damage if your hand slips when you are pressing down hard with a blunt knife. For basic, day-to-day use choose a good chopping knife, a small vegetable knife and a long serrated bread knife. If possible store knives safely in well-secured slotted racks. Drawer storage is not good for knives as the blades can easily become damaged when they are knocked around. If you do have to keep knives in a drawer, make sure they are stored with their handles

towards the front for safe lifting and keep the blades protected in some way. Good sharp knives are essential and indispensable pieces of kitchen equipment, so it is worth taking care of them.

A few of the recipes in this book call for the use of a food processor, which does save time and effort but is not strictly necessary. Other essential pieces of kitchen equipment which almost seem too obvious to mention include chopping boards, a colander, a sieve, a grater, a whisk and some means of extracting citrus juice, be this a squeezer or a juicer.

For the cook who likes to cook speedily and efficiently, where you store your equipment is an important factor to consider. I use my cooker as the pivot around which most of the action takes place. Pots, pans, whisks, spoons and strainers hang conveniently overhead within easy reach, a chopping board is on an adjacent work surface and ceramic pots hold a variety of wooden spoons, spatulas, ladles, scissors, peelers and other kitchen utensils, again all within easy reach.

wooden spatula

ladle

scissors

knives and peelers

vegetable knife

bread knife

whisks

draining
spoon

serving
spoon

chopping
board

grater

colander

wok

saucepans

frying pan

Make a Meal of It

The recipes in this book, although conceived as fast food, are equally suitable for entertaining. In fact, the ease and speed of preparation makes them the perfect choice when entertaining, allowing the cook more time to enjoy the company instead of being confined to the kitchen. Most of the recipes make a satisfying meal when served solo or with a simple side salad, while others may require a side order of pasta, rice or potatoes. Should you wish to serve a number of courses, I have compiled a few simple-to-make starters and desserts, followed by a selection of menus suggesting the appropriate dishes with which to serve them.

STARTERS

Lightly poached asparagus with crème fraîche and lemon.

Warm focaccia bread accompanied with olive oil, salt crystals and black olives.

Grilled cherry tomatoes served with salad and basil leaves, drizzled with a little dressing.

Crudités of celery, carrot, baby sweetcorn and mange-touts served with mayonnaise with a little pesto stirred through.

Thin slices of French bread, topped with tapenade (black olive paste) and mozzarella, then grilled and served hot.

Ready-made houmus and tzatziki served as dips with strips of warm pitta bread and black olives.

Chopped fresh tomatoes and onion flavoured with chopped fresh coriander and served with poppadums.

DESSERTS

Slices of sticky ginger cake warmed through in the microwave and served with a little golden syrup and cream.

Fresh summer berries, sprinkled with Kirsch and vanilla sugar, served with crème fraîche or natural yogurt.

Sweetened whipped cream flavoured with passion fruit and served on banana slices. Add amaretti biscuits for contrast.

A slice of Swiss roll topped with a scoop of ice cream, covered in stiff meringue and grilled until golden.

Banana slices and orange segments topped with a little apricot jam, wrapped in foil and baked in a hot oven for 10 minutes. Serve with cream.

Fresh blackberries crushed lightly with a fork and gently folded into softly whipped cream. Add a drizzle of Cassis (optional) and sugar to taste.

Brandy snap baskets filled with raspberries and peach slices, topped with a swirl of cream and a sprig of mint.

Ripe plums, halved, sprinkled with brandy and filled with mascarpone cheese. The plums are topped with chopped nuts and demerara sugar then grilled until the sugar has melted.

Menus for Entertaining

When you have guests to feed, expand your 15-minute vegetarian main course into an impressive meal. The menu suggestions below feature main course 15-minute vegetarian meals accompanied by quick and easy starters, accompaniments and desserts.

Menu 1

Warm focaccia bread with salt crystals and olives

Asparagus Rolls with Herb Butter Sauce

Lentil Stir-fry served with a green salad

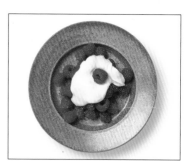

Summer berries with Kirsch and vanilla sugar

Menu 2

Grilled cherry tomato and basil salad

Mushrooms with Leeks and Stilton

Potato, Broccoli and Red Pepper Stir-fry

Baked banana and orange segments

Menu 3

Poached asparagus with crème fraîche and lemon

Ciabatta Rolls with Courgettes and Saffron

Red Fried Rice

Warm ginger cake with golden syrup

Menu 4

French bread slices with tapenade and mozzarella

Lemon and Parmesan Cappellini with Herb Bread

Fresh Spinach and Avocado Salad

Banana and amaretti with passion fruit cream

Menu 5

Fresh tomato and coriander with poppadoms

Bengali-style Vegetables

Cumin-spiced Marrow and Spinach

Spiced potato and cauliflower
Fresh fruit to follow

Menu 6

Crudités with mayonnaise dip

Potato, Spinach and Pine Nut Gratin

Vegetable Kebabs with Mustard and Honey

Grilled mascarpone plums

Deep-fried Courgettes with Chilli Sauce

Crunchy coated courgettes are great served with a fiery tomato sauce.

Serves 2

INGREDIENTS
15 ml/1 tbsp olive oil
1 onion, finely chopped
1 red chilli, seeded and finely diced
10 ml/2 tsp hot chilli powder
400 g/14 oz can chopped tomatoes
1 vegetable stock cube
50 ml/2 fl oz/¼ cup hot water
450 g/1 lb courgettes
150 ml/¼ pint/⅔ cup milk
50 g/2 oz/½ cup plain flour
oil for deep-frying
salt and freshly ground black pepper
thyme sprigs, to garnish

TO SERVE
lettuce leaves
watercress sprigs
slices of seeded bread

courgettes

chopped tomatoes

onion

red chilli

plain flour

stock cube

milk

chilli powder

1 Heat the oil in a pan. Add the onion and cook for 2–3 minutes. Add the chilli. Stir in the chilli powder and cook for 30 seconds.

2 Add the tomatoes. Crumble in the stock cube and stir in the water. Cover and cook for 10 minutes.

3 Meanwhile, top and tail the courgettes. Cut into 5 mm/¼ in slices.

4 Pour the milk into one shallow dish and spread out the flour in another. Dip the courgettes first in the milk, then into the flour, until well-coated.

5 Heat the oil for deep-frying to 180°C/350°F or until a cube of bread, when added to the oil, browns in 30–45 seconds. Add the courgettes in batches and deep-fry for 3–4 minutes until crisp. Drain on kitchen paper.

6 Place two or three lettuce leaves on each serving plate. Add a few sprigs of watercress and fan out the bread slices to one side. Season the sauce, spoon some on to each plate, top with the crisp courgettes and garnish with the thyme sprigs. Serve at once with salad and bread.

Cumin-spiced Marrow and Spinach

Tender chunks of marrow with spinach in a creamy, cumin-flavoured sauce.

Serves 2

INGREDIENTS
$^1/_2$ marrow, about 450 g/1 lb
30 ml/2 tbsp vegetable oil
10 ml/2 tsp cumin seeds
1 small red chilli, seeded and
   finely chopped
30 ml/2 tbsp water
50 g/2 oz tender young
   spinach leaves
90 ml/6 tbsp single cream
salt and freshly ground black pepper

spinach leaves

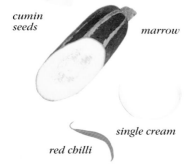

cumin seeds

marrow

single cream

red chilli

1 Peel the marrow and cut it in half. Scoop out the seeds. Cut the flesh into cubes.

2 Heat the oil in a large frying pan. Add the cumin seeds and the chopped chilli. Cook for 1 minute.

3 Add the marrow and water to the pan. Cover with foil or a lid and simmer for 8 minutes, stirring occasionally, until the marrow is just tender. Remove the cover and cook for 2 minutes more or until most of the water has evaporated.

4 Put the spinach leaves in a colander. Rinse well under cold water, drain and pat dry with kitchen paper. Tear into rough pieces.

5 Add the spinach to the marrow, replace the cover and cook gently for 1 minute. Serve hot.

COOK'S TIP
Be careful when handling chillies as the juice can burn sensitive skin. Wear rubber gloves or wash hands thoroughly after preparation.

6 Stir in the cream and cook over a high heat for 2 minutes. Add salt and pepper to taste, and serve. An Indian rice dish would be a good accompaniment. Alternatively, serve with naan bread.

Chilli Beans with Basmati Rice

Red kidney beans, tomatoes and chilli make a great combination. Serve with pasta or pitta bread instead of rice, if you prefer.

Serves 4

INGREDIENTS
350 g/12 oz/2 cups basmati rice
30 ml/2 tbsp olive oil
1 large onion, chopped
1 garlic clove, crushed
15 ml/1 tbsp hot chilli powder
15 ml/1 tbsp plain flour
15 ml/1 tbsp tomato purée
400 g/14 oz can chopped tomatoes
400 g/14 oz can red kidney
  beans, drained
150 ml/¼ pint/⅔ cup hot
  vegetable stock
chopped fresh parsley, to garnish
salt and freshly ground black pepper

basmati rice

chopped tomatoes

chilli powder

onion

tomato purée

garlic clove

stock cube

red kidney beans

plain flour

1 Wash the rice several times under cold running water. Drain well. Bring a large pan of water to the boil. Add the rice and cook for 10–12 minutes, until tender. Meanwhile, heat the oil in a frying pan. Add the onion and garlic and cook for 2 minutes.

2 Stir the chilli powder and flour into the onion and garlic mixture. Cook for 2 minutes, stirring frequently.

3 Stir in the tomato purée and chopped tomatoes. Rinse the kidney beans under cold water, drain well and add to the pan with the hot vegetable stock. Cover and cook for 12 minutes, stirring occasionally.

4 Season the chilli sauce with salt and pepper. Drain the rice and serve at once, with the chilli beans, sprinkled with a little chopped fresh parsley.

Spicy Cauliflower and Potato Salad

A delicious cold vegetable salad with a hot spicy dressing.

Serves 2–3

INGREDIENTS

1 medium cauliflower
2 medium potatoes
7.5 ml/1½ tsp caraway seeds
5 ml/1 tsp ground coriander
2.5 ml/½ tsp hot chilli powder
juice of 1 lemon
60 ml/4 tbsp olive oil
salt and freshly ground black pepper

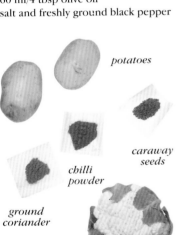

potatoes

caraway seeds

chilli powder

ground coriander

lemon

cauliflower

1 Break the cauliflower into small florets. Peel the potatoes and cut them into chunks.

2 Bring a large pan of water to the boil. Add the cauliflower florets and potato chunks and cook for 8 minutes until just tender.

3 Meanwhile, heat a non-stick frying pan. Add the caraway seeds and fry, shaking the pan constantly, for 1 minute. Tip the roasted seeds into a bowl and add the ground coriander and chilli powder, with salt and pepper to taste. Stir in the lemon juice and olive oil and mix to a paste.

4 Drain the vegetables well. Add them to the bowl and toss to coat in the chilli dressing. Serve at once, with hot pitta bread or brown rice.

Bengali-style Vegetables

A hot dry curry using spices that do not require long slow cooking.

Serves 4

INGREDIENTS

$1/2$ medium cauliflower, broken into small florets
1 large potato, peeled and cut into 2.5 cm/1 in dice
115 g/4 oz French beans, trimmed
2 courgettes, halved lengthways and sliced
2 green chillies
2.5 cm/1 in piece of fresh root ginger, peeled
120 ml/4 fl oz/$1/2$ cup natural yogurt
10 ml/2 tsp ground coriander
2.5 ml/$1/2$ tsp ground turmeric
25 g/1 oz/2 tbsp ghee
2.5 ml/$1/2$ tsp garam masala
5 ml/1 tsp cumin seeds
10 ml/2 tsp sugar
pinch each of ground cloves, ground cinnamon and ground cardamom
salt and freshly ground black pepper

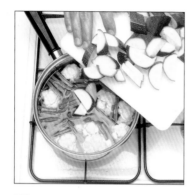

1 Bring a large pan of water to the boil. Add the cauliflower and potato and cook for 5 minutes. Add the beans and courgettes and cook for 2–3 minutes.

2 Meanwhile, cut the chillies in half, remove the seeds and roughly chop the flesh. Finely chop the ginger. Mix the chillies and ginger in a small bowl.

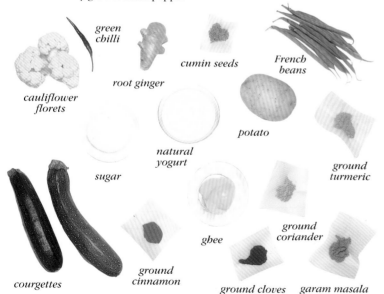

green chilli

root ginger

cumin seeds

cauliflower florets

French beans

potato

natural yogurt

sugar

ground turmeric

courgettes

ground cinnamon

ghee

ground coriander

ground cloves

garam masala

3 Drain the vegetables and tip them into a bowl. Add the chilli and ginger mixture, with the yogurt, ground coriander and turmeric. Season with plenty of salt and pepper and mix well.

4 Heat the ghee in a large frying pan. Add the vegetable mixture and cook over a high heat for 2 minutes, stirring from time to time.

5 Stir in the garam masala and cumin seeds and cook for 2 minutes.

6 Stir in the sugar and remaining spices and cook for 1 minute or until all the liquid has evaporated.

COOK'S TIP
If ghee is not available you can clarify your own butter. Melt 50 g/2 oz/¼ cup butter slowly in a small pan. Remove from the heat and leave for about 5 minutes. Pour off the clear yellow clarified butter, leaving the sediment in the pan.

Vegetable Fajita

A colourful medley of mushrooms and peppers in a spicy sauce, wrapped in tortillas and served with creamy guacamole.

Serves 2

INGREDIENTS
1 onion
1 red pepper
1 green pepper
1 yellow pepper
·1 garlic clove, crushed
225 g/8 oz mushrooms
90 ml/6 tbsp vegetable oil
30 ml/2 tbsp medium chilli powder
salt and freshly ground black pepper
coriander sprigs and 1 lime, cut into
    wedges, to garnish

FOR THE GUACAMOLE
1 ripe avocado
1 shallot, roughly chopped
1 green chilli, seeded and
    roughly chopped
juice of 1 lime

TO SERVE
4–6 flour tortillas, warmed

green
pepper

yellow
pepper

red pepper

mushrooms

green chilli

garlic
clove

shallot

avocado

lime

chilli powder

onion

1 Slice the onion. Cut the peppers in half, remove the seeds and cut the flesh into strips. Combine the onion and peppers in a bowl. Add the crushed garlic and mix lightly.

2 Remove the mushroom stalks. Save for making stock, or discard. Slice the mushroom caps and add to the pepper mixture in the bowl. Mix the oil and chilli powder in a cup, pour over the vegetable mixture and stir well. Set aside.

3 Make the guacamole. Cut the avocado in half and remove the stone and the peel. Put the flesh into a food processor or blender with the shallot, green chilli and lime juice. Process for 1 minute until smooth. Scrape into a small bowl, cover closely and put in the fridge to chill until required.

4 Heat a frying pan or wok until very hot. Add the marinated vegetables and stir-fry over high heat for 5–6 minutes until the mushrooms and pepper are just tender. Season well. Spoon a little of the filling on to each tortilla and roll up. Garnish with fresh coriander and lime wedges and serve with the guacamole.

Curried Eggs

Hard-boiled eggs are served on a bed of mild creamy sauce with a hint of curry.

Serves 2

INGREDIENTS
4 eggs
15 ml/1 tbsp sunflower oil
1 small onion, finely chopped
2.5 cm/1 in piece of fresh root
  ginger, peeled and grated
2.5 ml/¹/₂ tsp ground cumin
2.5 ml/¹/₂ tsp garam masala
25 ml/1¹/₂ tbsp tomato purée
10 ml/2 tsp tandoori paste
10 ml/2 tsp lemon juice
50 ml/2 fl oz/¹/₄ cup single cream
15 ml/1 tbsp chopped
  fresh coriander
salt and freshly ground black pepper
coriander sprigs, to garnish

eggs   *root ginger*   *garam masala*

fresh coriander

ground cumin

single cream

tomato purée

lemon

tandoori paste

onion

1 Put the eggs in a pan of water. Bring to the boil, lower the heat and simmer for 10 minutes.

2 Meanwhile, heat the oil in a frying pan. Cook the onion for 2–3 minutes. Add the ginger and cook for 1 minute.

3 Stir in the ground cumin, garam masala, tomato purée, tandoori paste, lemon juice and cream. Cook for 1–2 minutes, then stir in the coriander. Add salt and pepper to taste.

4 Drain the eggs, remove the shells and cut each egg in half. Spoon the sauce into a serving bowl, top with the eggs and garnish with the fresh coriander. Serve at once.

Breaded Aubergine with Hot Vinaigrette

Crisp on the outside, beautifully tender within, these aubergine slices taste wonderful with a spicy dressing flavoured with chilli and capers.

COOK'S TIP
When serving a salad with a warm dressing use robust leaves that will stand up to the heat.

Serves 2

INGREDIENTS
1 large aubergine
50 g/2 oz/½ cup plain flour
2 eggs, beaten
115 g/4 oz/2 cups fresh
  white breadcrumbs
vegetable oil for frying
1 head radicchio
salt and freshly ground black pepper

FOR THE DRESSING
30 ml/2 tbsp olive oil
1 garlic clove, crushed
15 ml/1 tbsp capers, drained
15 ml/1 tbsp white wine vinegar
15 ml/1 tbsp chilli oil

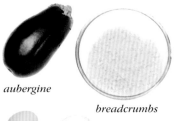

aubergine

breadcrumbs

plain flour

eggs

radicchio

capers

white wine vinegar

garlic clove

1 Top and tail the aubergine. Cut it into 5 mm/¼ in slices. Set aside.

2 Season the flour with a generous amount of salt and black pepper. Spread out in a shallow dish. Pour the beaten eggs into a second dish, and spread out the breadcrumbs in a third.

3 Dip the aubergine slices in the flour, then in the beaten egg and finally in the breadcrumbs, patting them on to make an even coating.

4 Pour vegetable oil into a large frying pan to a depth of about 5 mm/¼ in. Heat the oil, then fry the aubergine slices for 3–4 minutes, turning once. Drain on kitchen paper.

5 Heat the olive oil in a small pan. Add the garlic and the capers and cook over gentle heat for 1 minute. Increase the heat, add the vinegar and cook for 30 seconds. Stir in the chilli oil and remove the pan from the heat.

6 Arrange the radicchio leaves on two plates. Top with the hot aubergine slices. Drizzle over the vinaigrette and serve.

Double Tomato Tagliatelle

Sun-dried tomatoes add pungency to this dish, while the grilled fresh tomatoes add bite.

Serves 4

INGREDIENTS
45 ml/3 tbsp olive oil
1 garlic clove, crushed
1 small onion, chopped
50 ml/2 fl oz/¼ cup dry white wine
6 sun-dried tomatoes, chopped
30 ml/2 tbsp chopped fresh parsley
50 g/2 oz/½ cup stoned black
   olives, halved
450 g/1 lb fresh tagliatelle
4 tomatoes, halved
Parmesan cheese, to serve
salt and freshly ground black pepper

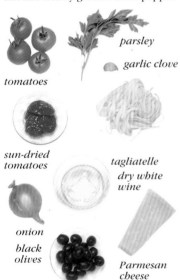

parsley

garlic clove

tomatoes

sun-dried tomatoes

tagliatelle

dry white wine

onion

black olives

Parmesan cheese

COOK'S TIP
It is essential to buy Parmesan in a piece for this dish. Find a good source – fresh Parmesan should not be unacceptably hard – and shave or grate it yourself. The flavour will be much more intense than that of the ready-grated product.

1 Heat 30 ml/2 tbsp of the oil in a pan. Add the garlic and onion and cook for 2–3 minutes, stirring occasionally. Add the wine, sun-dried tomatoes and the parsley. Cook for 2 minutes. Stir in the black olives.

2 Bring a large pan of salted water to the boil. Add the fresh tagliatelle and cook for 2–3 minutes until just tender. Preheat the grill.

3 Put the tomatoes on a tray and brush with the remaining oil. Grill for 3–4 minutes.

4 Drain the pasta, return it to the pan and toss with the sauce. Serve with the grilled tomatoes, freshly ground black pepper and shavings of Parmesan.

Penne with Fennel Concassé and Blue Cheese

The aniseed flavour of the fennel makes it the perfect partner for tomato, especially when topped with blue cheese.

Serves 2

INGREDIENTS
1 fennel bulb
225 g/8 oz penne or other dried
  pasta shapes
30 ml/2 tbsp extra virgin olive oil
1 shallot, finely chopped
300 ml/½ pint/1¼ cups passata
pinch of sugar
5 ml/1 tsp chopped fresh oregano
115 g/4 oz blue cheese
salt and freshly ground black pepper

oregano

shallot

fennel bulb

penne

passata

sugar

blue cheese

1 Cut the fennel bulb in half. Cut away the hard core and root. Slice the fennel thinly, then cut the slices into strips.

2 Bring a large pan of salted water to the boil. Add the pasta and cook for 10–12 minutes until just tender.

3 Meanwhile, heat the oil in a small saucepan. Add the fennel and shallot and cook for 2–3 minutes over a high heat, stirring occasionally.

4 Add the passata, sugar and oregano. Cover the pan and simmer gently for 10–12 minutes, until the fennel is tender. Add salt and pepper to taste. Drain the pasta and return it to the pan and toss with the sauce. Serve in bowls, with the blue cheese crumbled over the top.

Lemon and Parmesan Capellini with Herb Bread

Cream is thickened with Parmesan and flavoured with lemon to make a superb sauce for pasta.

Serves 2

INGREDIENTS
¹/₂ Granary baguette
50 g/2 oz/¹/₄ cup butter, softened
1 garlic clove, crushed
30 ml/2 tbsp chopped fresh herbs
225 g/8 oz dried or fresh capellini
250 ml/8 fl oz/1 cup single cream
75 g/3 oz Parmesan cheese, grated
finely grated rind of 1 lemon
salt and freshly ground black pepper

garlic clove

rosemary

Parmesan cheese

thyme

capellini

butter

lemon

single cream

Granary baguette   *parsley*   *oregano*

1 Preheat the oven to 200°C/400°F/ Gas 6. Cut the baguette into thick slices.

2 Put the butter in a bowl and beat with the garlic and herbs. Spread thickly over each slice of bread.

3 Reassemble the baguette. Wrap in foil, support on a baking sheet and bake for 10 minutes.

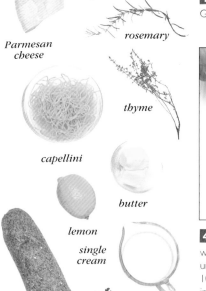

4 Meanwhile, bring a large pan of water to the boil and cook the pasta until just tender. Dried pasta will take 10–12 minutes; fresh pasta will be ready in 2–3 minutes.

5 Pour the cream into another pan and bring to the boil. Stir in the Parmesan and lemon rind. The sauce should thicken in about 30 seconds.

6 Drain the pasta, return it to the pan and toss with the sauce. Season to taste and sprinkle with a little chopped fresh parsley and grated lemon rind, if liked. Serve with the hot herb bread.

Summer Pasta Salad

Tender young vegetables in a light dressing make a delicious lunch.

Serves 2–3

INGREDIENTS

225 g/8 oz fusilli or other dried
   pasta shapes
115 g/4 oz baby carrots, trimmed
   and halved
115 g/4 oz baby sweetcorn, halved
   lengthways
50 g/2 oz mange-touts
115 g/4 oz young asparagus
   spears, trimmed
4 spring onions, trimmed
   and shredded
10 ml/2 tsp white wine vinegar
60 ml/4 tbsp extra virgin olive oil
15 ml/1 tbsp wholegrain mustard
salt and freshly ground black pepper

spring onions

young asparagus

fusilli

baby carrots

wholegrain mustard

baby sweetcorn

white wine vinegar

mange-touts

1 Bring a large pan of salted water to the boil. Add the pasta and cook for 10–12 minutes, until just tender. Meanwhile, cook the carrots and sweetcorn in a second pan of boiling salted water for 5 minutes.

2 Add the mange-touts and asparagus to the carrot mixture and cook for 2–3 minutes more. Drain all the vegetables and refresh under cold running water. Drain again.

3 Tip the vegetable mixture into a mixing bowl, add the spring onions and toss well together.

4 Drain the pasta, refresh it under cold running water and drain again. Toss with the vegetables. Mix the vinegar, olive oil and mustard in a jar. Add salt and pepper to taste, close the jar tightly and shake well. Pour the dressing over the salad. Toss well and serve.

Five-spice Vegetable Noodles

Vary this vegetable stir-fry by substituting mushrooms, bamboo shoots, beansprouts, mange-touts or water chestnuts for some or all of the vegetables suggested below.

Serves 2–3

INGREDIENTS
225 g/8 oz dried egg noodles
30 ml/2 tbsp sesame oil
2 carrots
1 celery stick
1 small fennel bulb
2 courgettes, halved and sliced
1 red chilli, seeded and chopped
2.5 cm/1 in piece of fresh root
  ginger, peeled and grated
1 garlic clove, crushed
7.5 ml/1½ tsp Chinese five-spice
  powder
2.5 ml/½ tsp ground cinnamon
4 spring onions, sliced
50 ml/2 fl oz/¼ cup warm water

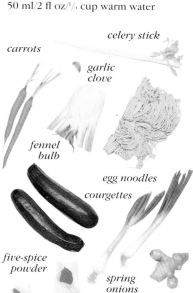

carrots
celery stick
garlic clove
fennel bulb
egg noodles
courgettes
five-spice powder
spring onions
cinnamon
root ginger

1 Bring a large pan of salted water to the boil. Add the noodles and cook for 2–3 minutes until just tender. Drain the noodles, return them to the pan and toss in a little of the oil. Set aside.

2 Cut the carrot and celery into julienne. Cut the fennel bulb in half and cut out the hard core. Cut into slices, then cut the slices into julienne.

3 Heat the remaining oil in a wok or frying pan until very hot. Add all the vegetables, including the chilli, and stir-fry for 7–8 minutes.

4 Add the ginger and garlic and stir-fry for 2 minutes, then add the spices. Cook for 1 minute. Add the spring onions and stir-fry for 1 minute. Pour in the warm water and cook for 1 minute. Stir in the noodles and toss well together. Serve sprinkled with sliced red chilli, if liked.

Mushroom Bolognese

A quick – and exceedingly tasty – vegetarian
version of the classic Italian meat dish.

Serves 4

INGREDIENTS
450 g/1 lb mushrooms
15 ml/1 tbsp olive oil
1 onion, chopped
1 garlic clove, crushed
15 ml/1 tbsp tomato purée
400 g/14 oz can chopped tomatoes
15 ml/1 tbsp chopped fresh oregano
450 g/1 lb fresh pasta
Parmesan cheese, to serve
chopped fresh oregano, to garnish

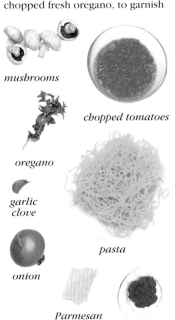

mushrooms

chopped tomatoes

oregano

garlic
clove

pasta

onion

Parmesan
cheese

tomato
purée

1 Trim the mushroom stems neatly,
then cut each mushroom into quarters.

2 Heat the oil in a large pan. Add the
chopped onion and garlic and cook for
2–3 minutes.

3 Add the mushrooms to the pan and
cook over a high heat for 3–4 minutes,
stirring occasionally.

4 Stir in the tomato purée, chopped
tomatoes and oregano. Lower the heat,
cover and cook for 5 minutes.

5 Meanwhile, bring a large pan of
salted water to the boil. Cook the pasta
for 2–3 minutes until just tender.

COOK'S TIP

If you prefer to use dried pasta, make this the first thing that you cook. It will take 10–12 minutes, during which time you can make the mushroom mixture. Use 350 g/12 oz dried pasta.

6 Season the bolognese sauce with salt and pepper. Drain the pasta, tip it into a bowl and add the mushroom mixture. Toss to mix. Serve in individual bowls, topped with shavings of fresh Parmesan cheese and a sprinkling of chopped fresh oregano.

Fried Noodles with Beansprouts and Asparagus

Soft fried noodles contrast beautifully with crisp beansprouts and asparagus.

Serves 2

INGREDIENTS

115 g/4 oz dried egg noodles
60 ml/4 tbsp vegetable oil
1 small onion, chopped
2.5 cm/1 in piece of fresh root
  ginger, peeled and grated
2 garlic cloves, crushed
175 g/6 oz young asparagus
  spears, trimmed
115 g/4 oz beansprouts
4 spring onions, sliced
45 ml/3 tbsp soy sauce
salt and freshly ground black pepper

onion

spring onions

garlic cloves

root ginger

soy sauce

beansprouts

egg noodles

asparagus spears

1 Bring a pan of salted water to the boil. Add the noodles and cook for 2–3 minutes, until just tender. Drain and toss in 30 ml/2 tbsp of the oil.

2 Heat the remaining oil in a wok or frying pan until very hot. Add the onion, ginger and garlic and stir-fry for 2–3 minutes. Add the asparagus and stir-fry for a further 2–3 minutes.

3 Add the noodles and beansprouts and stir-fry for 2 minutes.

4 Stir in the spring onions and soy sauce. Season to taste, adding salt sparingly as the soy sauce will add quite a salty flavour. Stir-fry for 1 minute, then serve at once.

COOK'S TIP

Add a dash of vinegar to the water before poaching the eggs. This helps to keep the whites together. To ensure that a poached egg has a good shape, swirl the water with a spoon, whirlpool-fashion, before sliding in the egg.

6 Place a poached egg on each salad. Scatter with shavings of Parmesan and a little freshly ground black pepper, if liked.

Classic Greek Salad

If you have ever visited Greece you'll know that a Greek salad with a chunk of bread makes a delicious, filling meal.

Serves 4

INGREDIENTS
1 cos lettuce
$^1/_2$ cucumber, halved lengthways
4 tomatoes
8 spring onions
75 g/3 oz/2$^1/_2$ cups Greek
  black olives
115 g/4 oz feta cheese
90 ml/6 tbsp white wine vinegar
150 ml/$^1/_4$ pint/$^2/_3$ cup extra virgin
  olive oil
salt and freshly ground black pepper

tomatoes

cos lettuce

feta cheese

black olives

white wine vinegar

cucumber

spring onions

COOK'S TIP
The salad can be assembled in advance and chilled, but should only be dressed just before serving. Keep the dressing at room temperature as chilling deadens its flavour.

1 Tear the lettuce leaves into pieces and place them in a large mixing bowl. Slice the cucumber and add to the bowl.

2 Cut the tomatoes into wedges and put them into the bowl.

3 Slice the spring onions. Add them to the bowl with the olives and toss well.

4 Cut the feta cheese into cubes and add to the salad.

5 Put the vinegar, olive oil and seasoning into a small bowl and whisk well. Pour the dressing over the salad and toss to combine. Serve at once, with extra olives and chunks of bread, if liked.

Chicory, Fruit and Nut Salad

Mildly bitter chicory is wonderful with sweet fruit, and is especially delicious when complemented by a creamy curry sauce.

Serves 4

INGREDIENTS

45 ml/3 tbsp mayonnaise
15 ml/1 tbsp Greek yogurt
15 ml/1 tbsp mild curry paste
90 ml/6 tbsp single cream
$^1/_2$ iceberg lettuce
2 heads of chicory
50 g/2 oz/$^1/_2$ cup cashew nuts
50 g/2 oz/1$^1/_4$ cups flaked coconut
2 red apples
75 g/3 oz/$^1/_2$ cup currants

currants

iceberg lettuce

curry paste *mayonnaise*

cashew nuts *red apples*

single cream *flaked coconut*

chicory

1 Mix the mayonnaise, Greek yogurt, curry paste and single cream in a small bowl. Cover and chill until required.

2 Tear the iceberg lettuce into pieces and put into a mixing bowl.

3 Cut the root end off each head of chicory, separate the leaves and add them to the lettuce. Preheat the grill.

4 Toast the cashew nuts for 2 minutes until golden. Tip into a bowl and set aside. Spread out the coconut flakes on a baking sheet. Grill for 1 minute until golden.

5 Quarter the apples and cut out the cores. Slice the apples and add to the lettuce with the coconut, cashew nuts and currants.

COOK'S TIP
Watch the coconut and cashew nuts very carefully when grilling, as they brown very fast.

6 Spoon the dressing over the salad, toss lightly and serve.

Grilled Pepper Salad

Grilled peppers are delicious served hot with a sharp dressing. You can also serve them cold.

Serves 2

INGREDIENTS
1 red pepper
1 green pepper
1 yellow or orange pepper
$^1/_2$ radicchio, separated into leaves
$^1/_2$ frisée, separated into leaves
7.5 ml/1$^1/_2$ tsp white wine vinegar
30 ml/2 tbsp extra virgin olive oil
175 g/6 oz goat's cheese
salt and freshly ground black pepper

frisée

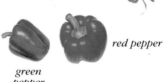

green pepper

red pepper

yellow pepper

goat's cheese

white wine vinegar

radicchio

1 Preheat the grill. Cut all the peppers in half. Cut each half into pieces.

2 Put the pepper pieces on a rack set over a grill pan. Grill for 10 minutes.

3 Meanwhile, divide the radicchio and frisée leaves between two plates. Chill until required.

4 Mix the vinegar and olive oil in a jar. Add salt and pepper to taste, close the jar tightly and shake well.

5 Slice the goat's cheese, place on a baking sheet and grill for 1 minute.

6 Arrange the peppers and grilled goat's cheese on the salads. Pour over the dressing and grind a little extra black pepper over each.

COOK'S TIP
Grill the peppers until they just start to blacken around the edges – don't let them burn.

Courgettes, Carrots and Pecans in Pitta Bread

Chunks of fried courgette served with a tangy salad in pitta pockets.

Serves 2

INGREDIENTS
2 carrots
25 g/1 oz/¹/₄ cup pecan nuts
4 spring onions, sliced
50 ml/2 fl oz/¹/₄ cup Greek yogurt
35 ml/7 tsp olive oil
5 ml/1 tsp lemon juice
15 ml/1 tbsp chopped fresh mint
2 courgettes
25 g/1 oz/¹/₄ cup plain flour
2 pitta breads
salt and freshly ground black pepper
shredded lettuce, to serve

courgettes

spring onions

pecan nuts   lemon

mint

Greek yogurt

carrots

1 Top and tail the carrots. Grate them coarsely into a bowl.

2 Stir in the pecans and spring onions and toss well.

3 In a clean bowl, whisk the yogurt with 7.5 ml/1¹/₂ tsp of the olive oil, the lemon juice and the fresh mint. Stir the dressing into the carrot mixture and mix well. Cover and chill until required.

4 Top and tail the courgettes. Cut them diagonally into slices. Season the flour with salt and pepper. Spread it out on a plate and coat the courgette slices.

COOK'S TIP
Do not fill the pitta breads too soon or the carrot mixture will make the bread soggy.

5 Heat the remaining oil in a large frying pan. Add the coated courgette slices and cook for 3–4 minutes, turning once, until browned. Drain the courgettes on kitchen paper.

6 Make a slit in each pitta bread to form a pocket. Fill the pittas with the carrot mixture and the courgette slices. Serve on a bed of shredded lettuce.

Courgette Puffs with Salad and Balsamic Dressing

This unusual salad consists of deep-fried courgettes, flavoured with mint and served warm on a bed of salad leaves with a balsamic dressing.

Serves 2

INGREDIENTS
450 g/1 lb courgettes
75 g/3 oz/1½ cups fresh white breadcrumbs
1 egg
pinch of cayenne pepper
15 ml/1 tbsp chopped fresh mint
oil for deep-frying
15 ml/1 tbsp/3 tbsp balsamic vinegar
45 ml/3 tbsp extra virgin olive oil
200 g/7 oz mixed salad leaves
salt and freshly ground black pepper

courgettes

white breadcrumbs

balsamic vinegar

mixed salad leaves

egg

mint

1 Top and tail the courgettes. Coarsely grate them and put into a colander. Squeeze out the excess water, then put the courgettes into a bowl.

2 Add the breadcrumbs, egg, cayenne, mint and seasoning. Mix well.

3 Shape the courgette mixture into balls, about the size of walnuts.

4 Heat the oil for deep-frying to 180°C/350°F or until a cube of bread, when added to the oil, browns in 30–40 seconds. Deep-fry the courgette balls in batches for 2–3 minutes. Drain on kitchen paper.

5 Whisk the vinegar and oil together and season well.

6 Put the salad leaves in a bowl and pour over the dressing. Add the courgette puffs and toss lightly together. Serve at once, while the courgette puffs are still crisp.

Vegetable and Satay Salad

Baby new potatoes, tender vegetables and crunchy chick-peas are smothered in a creamy peanut dressing.

Serves 4

INGREDIENTS
450 g/1 lb baby new potatoes
1 small head cauliflower, broken
  into small florets
225 g/8 oz French beans, trimmed
400 g/14 oz can chick-peas, drained
115 g/4 oz watercress sprigs
115 g/4 oz beansprouts
8 spring onions, sliced
60 ml/4 tbsp crunchy peanut butter
150 ml/¼ pint/⅔ cup hot water
5 ml/1 tsp chilli sauce
10 ml/2 tsp soft brown sugar
5 ml/1 tsp soy sauce
5 ml/1 tsp lime juice

cauliflower

watercress

soy
sauce

spring
onions

crunchy
peanut butter

soft brown
sugar

chick-
peas

beansprouts

chilli
sauce

lime

French
beans

baby new
potatoes

1 Put the potatoes into a pan and add water to just cover. Bring to the boil and cook for 10–12 minutes or until the potatoes are just tender when pierced with the point of a sharp knife. Drain and refresh under cold running water. Drain once again.

2 Meanwhile, bring another pan of salted water to the boil. Add the cauliflower and cook for 5 minutes, then add the beans and cook for 5 minutes more. Drain both vegetables, refresh under cold water and drain again.

3 Put the cauliflower and beans into a large bowl and add the chick-peas. Halve the potatoes and add. Toss lightly. Mix the watercress, beansprouts and spring onions together. Divide between four plates and pile the vegetables on top.

4 Put the peanut butter into a bowl and stir in the water. Add the chilli sauce, brown sugar, soy sauce and lime juice. Whisk well then drizzle the dressing over the vegetables.

Fresh Spinach and Avocado Salad

Young tender spinach leaves make a change from lettuce and are delicious served with avocado, cherry tomatoes and radishes in a tofu sauce.

Serves 2-3

INGREDIENTS
1 large avocado
juice of 1 lime
225 g/8 oz fresh baby spinach leaves
115 g/4 oz cherry tomatoes
4 spring onions, sliced
1/2 cucumber
50 g/2 oz radishes, sliced

FOR THE DRESSING
115 g/4 oz soft silken tofu
45 ml/3 tbsp milk
10 ml/2 tsp mustard
2.5 ml/1/2 tsp white wine vinegar
pinch of cayenne
salt and freshly ground black pepper

tofu spring onions spinach leaves

cherry tomatoes

avocado

white wine vinegar

mustard

cayenne lime

cucumber

radishes

milk

1 Cut the avocado in half, remove the stone and strip off the skin. Cut the flesh into slices. Transfer to a plate, drizzle over the lime juice and set aside.

2 Wash and dry the spinach leaves. Put them in a mixing bowl.

COOK'S TIP
Use soft silken tofu rather than the firm block variety. It can be found in most supermarkets in long-life cartons.

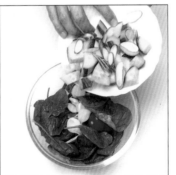

3 Cut the larger cherry tomatoes in half and add all the tomatoes to the mixing bowl, with the spring onions. Cut the cucumber into chunks and add to the bowl with the sliced radishes.

4 Make the dressing. Put the tofu, milk, mustard, wine vinegar and cayenne in a food processor or blender. Add salt and pepper to taste. Process for 30 seconds until smooth. Scrape the dressing into a bowl and add a little extra milk if you like a thinner dressing. Sprinkle with a little extra cayenne and garnish with radish roses and herb sprigs, if liked.

Asparagus Rolls with Herb Butter Sauce

For a taste sensation, try tender asparagus spears wrapped in crisp filo pastry. The buttery herb sauce makes the perfect accompaniment.

Serves 2

INGREDIENTS
4 sheets of filo pastry
50 g/2 oz/¹/₄ cup butter, melted
16 young asparagus spears, trimmed

FOR THE SAUCE
2 shallots, finely chopped
1 bay leaf
150 ml/¹/₄ pint/²/₃ cup dry white wine
175 g/6 oz butter, softened
15 ml/1 tbsp chopped fresh herbs
salt and freshly ground black pepper
snipped chives, to garnish

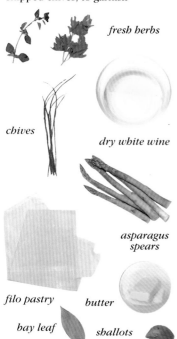

fresh herbs

chives

dry white wine

asparagus spears

filo pastry   *butter*

bay leaf   *shallots*

1 Preheat the oven to 200°C/400°F/ Gas 6. Brush each filo sheet with melted butter. Fold one corner of the sheet down to the bottom edge to give a wedge shape.

2 Lay 4 asparagus spears on top at the longest edge and roll up towards the shortest edge. Using the remaining filo and asparagus spears make 3 more rolls in the same way.

3 Lay the rolls on a greased baking sheet. Brush with the remaining melted butter. Bake in the oven for 8 minutes until golden.

4 Meanwhile, put the shallots, bay leaf and wine into a pan. Cover and cook over a high heat until the wine is reduced to about 45–60 ml/3–4 tbsp.

5 Strain the wine mixture into a bowl. Whisk in the butter, a little at a time, until the sauce is smooth and glossy.

6 Stir in the herbs and add salt and pepper to taste. Return to the pan and keep the sauce warm. Serve the rolls on individual plates with a salad garnish, if liked. Serve the butter sauce separately, sprinkled with a few snipped chives.

Tomato Omelette Envelopes

Delicious chive omelettes, folded and filled with tomato and melting Camembert cheese.

Serves 2

INGREDIENTS
1 small onion
4 tomatoes
30 ml/2 tbsp vegetable oil
4 eggs
30 ml/2 tbsp snipped fresh chives
115 g/4 oz Camembert cheese,
  rinded and diced
salt and freshly ground black pepper

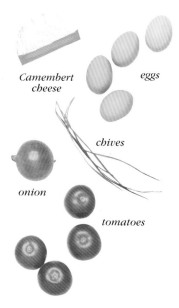

Camembert cheese

eggs

chives

onion

tomatoes

1 Cut the onion in half. Cut each half into thin wedges. Cut the tomatoes into wedges of similar size.

2 Heat 15 ml/1 tbsp of the oil in a frying pan. Cook the onion for 2 minutes over a moderate heat, then raise the heat and add the tomatoes. Cook for a further 2 minutes, then remove the pan from the heat.

3 Beat the eggs with the chives in a bowl. Add salt and pepper to taste. Heat the remaining oil in an omelette pan. Add half the egg mixture and tilt the pan to spread thinly. Cook for 1 minute.

4 Flip the omelette over and cook for 1 minute more. Remove from the pan and keep hot. Make a second omelette with the remaining egg mixture.

5 Return the tomato mixture to a high heat. Add the cheese and toss the mixture over the heat for 1 minute.

6 Divide the mixture between the omelettes and fold them over. Serve at once. Add crisp lettuce leaves and chunks of Granary bread, if liked.

COOK'S TIP
You may need to wipe the pan clean between the omelettes and reheat a little more oil.

Mushrooms with Leeks and Stilton

Upturned mushrooms make perfect containers for this leek and Stilton filling.

Serves 2–3

INGREDIENTS
1 leek, thinly sliced
6 flat mushrooms
2 garlic cloves, crushed
30 ml/2 tbsp chopped fresh parsley
115 g/4 oz/½ cup butter, softened
115 g/4 oz Stilton cheese
freshly ground black pepper
frisée and tomato halves, to garnish

leek

butter

flat mushrooms

parsley

Stilton cheese

garlic cloves

1 Put the leek slices in a small pan with a little water. Cover and cook for about 5 minutes until tender. Drain, refresh under cold water and drain again.

2 Remove the stalks from the mushrooms and set them aside. Put the mushroom caps, hollows uppermost, on an oiled baking sheet.

3 Put the mushroom stalks, garlic and parsley in a food processor or blender. Process for 1 minute. Tip into a bowl, add the leek and butter and season with freshly ground black pepper to taste. Preheat the grill.

4 Crumble the Stilton into the mushroom mixture and mix well. Divide the Stilton mixture between the mushroom caps and grill for 6–7 minutes until bubbling. Serve garnished with frisée and halved tomatoes.

Tomato and Okra Stew

Okra is an unusual and delicious vegetable. It releases a sticky sap when cooked, which helps to thicken the stew.

Serves 4

INGREDIENTS
15 ml/1 tbsp olive oil
1 onion, chopped
400 g/14 oz can pimientos, drained
2 x 400 g/14 oz cans chopped
 tomatoes
275 g/10 oz okra
30 ml/2 tbsp chopped fresh parsley
salt and freshly ground black pepper

parsley

chopped tomatoes

pimientos

onion

okra

1 Heat the oil in a pan. Add the onion and cook for 2–3 minutes.

2 Roughly chop the pimientos and add to the onion. Add the chopped tomatoes and mix well.

3 Cut the tops off the okra and cut into halves or quarters if large. Add to the tomato sauce in the pan. Season with plenty of salt and pepper.

4 Bring the vegetable stew to the boil, then lower the heat, cover the pan and simmer for 12 minutes until the vegetables are tender and the sauce has thickened. Stir in the chopped parsley and serve at once.

Vegetable Kebabs with Mustard and Honey

A colourful mixture of vegetables and tofu, skewered, glazed and grilled until tender.

Serves 4

INGREDIENTS
1 yellow pepper
2 small courgettes
225 g/8 oz piece of firm tofu
8 cherry tomatoes
8 button mushrooms
15 ml/1 tbsp wholegrain mustard
15 ml/1 tbsp clear honey
30 ml/2 tbsp olive oil
salt and freshly ground black pepper

TO SERVE
4 portions cooked mixed rice
  and wild rice
lime segments
flat leaf parsley

1 Cut the pepper in half and remove the seeds. Cut each half into quarters and cut each quarter in half.

2 Top and tail the courgettes and peel them decoratively, if you like. Cut each courgette into 8 chunks.

3 Cut the tofu into pieces of a similar size to the vegetables.

courgettes

cherry tomatoes

yellow pepper

clear honey

wholegrain mustard

button mushrooms

tofu

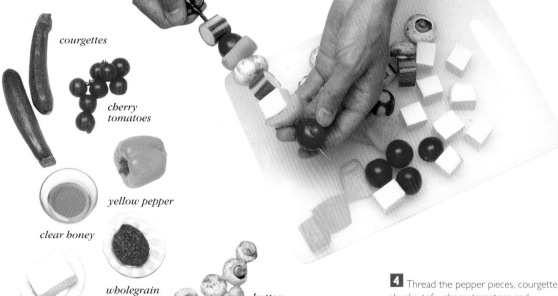

5 Whisk the mustard, honey and olive oil in a small bowl. Add salt and pepper to taste.

4 Thread the pepper pieces, courgette chunks, tofu, cherry tomatoes and mushrooms alternately on to four metal or bamboo skewers. Preheat the grill.

6 Put the kebabs on to a baking sheet. Brush with the mustard and honey glaze. Cook under the grill for 8 minutes, turning once or twice during cooking. Serve with a mixture of long grain and wild rice, and garnish with lime segments and parsley.

COOK'S TIP
If using bamboo skewers, soak them in a bowl of cold water before threading, to prevent them burning when placed under the grill.

Deep-fried Florets with Tangy Thyme Mayonnaise

Cauliflower and broccoli make a sensational snack when coated in a beer batter and deep-fried. Serve with a tangy mayonnaise.

Serves 2–3

INGREDIENTS
175 g/6 oz cauliflower
175 g/6 oz broccoli
2 eggs, separated
30 ml/2 tbsp olive oil
250 ml/8 fl oz/1 cup beer
150 ml/5 oz/1¼ cups plain flour
pinch of salt
30 ml/2 tbsp shredded fresh basil
vegetable oil for deep-frying
150 ml/¼ pint/⅔ cup good quality
  mayonnaise
10 ml/2 tsp chopped fresh thyme
10 ml/2 tsp grated lemon rind
10 ml/2 tsp lemon juice
sea salt, for sprinkling

eggs

basil

plain flour

mayonnaise

broccoli

cauliflower

beer

thyme

lemon

1 Break the cauliflower and broccoli into small florets, cutting large florets into smaller pieces. Set aside.

2 Beat the egg yolks, olive oil, beer, flour and salt in a bowl. Strain the batter if necessary, to remove any lumps.

3 Whisk the egg whites until stiff. Fold into the batter with the basil.

4 Heat the oil for deep-frying to 180°C/350°F or until a cube of bread, when added to the oil, browns in 30–45 seconds. Dip the florets in the batter and deep-fry in batches for 2–3 minutes until the coating is golden and crisp. Drain on kitchen paper.

5 Mix the mayonnaise, thyme, lemon rind and juice in a small bowl.

6 Sprinkle the florets with sea salt. Serve with the thyme and lemon mayonnaise.

Black Bean and Vegetable Stir-fry

The secret of a quick stir-fry is to prepare all the ingredients first. This colourful vegetable mixture is coated in a classic Chinese sauce.

Serves 4

INGREDIENTS
8 spring onions
225 g/8 oz/2 cups button
  mushrooms
1 red pepper
1 green pepper
2 large carrots
60 ml/4 tbsp sesame oil
2 garlic cloves, crushed
60 ml/4 tbsp black bean sauce
90 ml/6 tbsp warm water
225 g/8 oz beansprouts
salt and freshly ground black pepper

1 Thinly slice the spring onions and button mushrooms.

2 Cut both the peppers in half, remove the seeds and slice the flesh into thin strips.

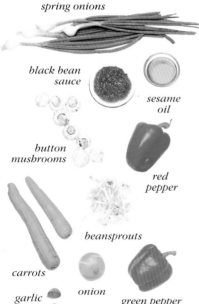

spring onions

black bean sauce

sesame oil

button mushrooms

red pepper

beansprouts

carrots

garlic cloves

onion

green pepper

3 Cut the carrots in half. Cut each half into thin strips lengthways. Stack the slices and cut through them to make very fine strips.

4 Heat the oil in a large wok or frying pan until very hot. Add the spring onions and garlic and stir-fry for 30 seconds.

5 Add the mushrooms, peppers and carrots. Stir-fry for 5–6 minutes over a high heat until the vegetables are just beginning to soften.

6 Mix the black bean sauce with the water. Add to the wok or pan and cook for 3–4 minutes. Stir in the beansprouts and stir-fry for 1 minute more, until all the vegetables are coated in the sauce. Season to taste. Serve at once.

COOK'S TIP
For best results the oil in the wok must be very hot before adding the vegetables.

French Bread Pizzas with Artichokes

Crunchy French bread makes an ideal base for these quick pizzas.

Serves 4

INGREDIENTS

15 ml/1 tbsp sunflower oil
1 onion, chopped
1 green pepper, seeded and
 chopped
200 g/7 oz can chopped tomatoes
15 ml/1 tbsp tomato purée
½ French stick
400 g/14 oz can artichoke
 hearts, drained
115 g/4 oz mozzarella cheese, sliced
15 ml/1 tbsp poppy seeds
salt and freshly ground black pepper

mozzarella cheese

French stick

tomato purée

chopped tomatoes

green pepper

poppy seeds

onion

artichoke hearts

1 Heat the oil in a frying pan. Add the chopped onion and pepper and cook for 4 minutes until just softened.

2 Stir in the chopped tomatoes and tomato purée. Cook for 4 minutes. Remove from the heat and add salt and pepper to taste.

3 Cut the piece of French stick in half lengthways. Cut each half in four to give eight pieces in all.

4 Spoon a little of the pepper and tomato mixture over each piece of bread. Preheat the grill.

5 Slice the artichoke hearts. Arrange them on top of the pepper and tomato mixture. Cover with the mozzarella slices and sprinkle with the poppy seeds.

6 Arrange the French bread pizzas on a rack over a grill pan and grill for 6–8 minutes until the cheese melts and is beginning to brown. Serve at once.

New Spring Salad

This chunky salad makes a satisfying meal, use other spring vegetables, if you like.

Serves 4

INGREDIENTS

675 g/1½ lb small new
   potatoes, halved
400 g/14 oz can broad
   beans, drained
115 g/4 oz cherry tomatoes
50 g/2 oz/2½ cups walnut halves
30 ml/2 tbsp white wine vinegar
15 ml/1 tbsp wholegrain mustard
60 ml/4 tbsp olive oil
pinch of sugar
225 g/8 oz young asparagus
   spears, trimmed
6 spring onions, trimmed
salt and freshly ground black pepper
baby spinach leaves, to serve

asparagus spears

new potatoes

wholegrain mustard

broad beans

cherry tomatoes

spring onions

walnut halves

I Put the potatoes in a pan. Cover with cold water and bring to the boil. Cook for 10–12 minutes, until tender. Meanwhile, tip the broad beans into a bowl. Cut the tomatoes in half and add them to the bowl with the walnuts.

2 Put the white wine vinegar, mustard, olive oil and sugar into a jar. Add salt and pepper to taste. Close the jar tightly and shake well.

3 Add the asparagus to the potatoes and cook for 3 minutes more. Drain the cooked vegetables well, cool under cold running water and drain again. Thickly slice the potatoes. Cut the spring onions into halves.

4 Add the asparagus, potatoes and spring onions to the bowl containing the broad bean mixture. Pour the dressing over the salad and toss well. Serve on a bed of baby spinach leaves.

Brioche with Mixed Mushrooms

Mushrooms in a rich sherry sauce, served on toasted brioche, make a delectable lunch, but would also serve 6 as a starter.

Serves 4

INGREDIENTS
75 g/3 oz/6 tbsp butter
1 vegetable stock cube
450 g/1 lb shiitake mushrooms,
  caps only, sliced
225 g/8 oz button
  mushrooms, sliced
45 ml/3 tbsp dry sherry
250 ml/8 fl oz/1 cup crème fraîche
10 ml/2 tsp lemon juice
8 thick slices of brioche
salt and freshly ground black pepper

shiitake and button mushrooms

brioche

butter

stock cube

lemon

crème fraîche

COOK'S TIP
If shiitake mushrooms are too expensive or not available, substitute more button or brown cap mushrooms. Wipe the mushrooms with kitchen paper before use.

1 Melt the butter in a large pan. Crumble in the stock cube and stir for about 30 seconds.

2 Add the shiitake and button mushrooms to the pan and cook for 5 minutes over a moderate to high heat, stirring occasionally.

3 Stir in the sherry. Cook for 1 minute, then add the crème fraîche. Cook, stirring, over a gentle heat for 5 minutes. Stir in the lemon juice and add salt and pepper to taste. Preheat the grill.

4 Toast the brioche slices under the grill until just golden on both sides. Spoon the mushrooms on top, flash briefly under the grill, and serve. Fresh thyme may be used to garnish, if liked.

Ratatouille with Soft Cheese Croûtons

Crisp croûtons and creamy Camembert provide a tasty topping on hot ratatouille. Choose a quality brand of ratatouille or make your own.

Serves 2

INGREDIENTS
3 thick slices of white bread
225 g/8 oz firm Camembert cheese
60 ml/4 tbsp olive oil
1 garlic clove, chopped
400 g/14 oz can ratatouille
parsley sprigs, to garnish

ratatouille

parsley

garlic clove

Camembert cheese

white bread

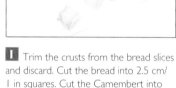

1 Trim the crusts from the bread slices and discard. Cut the bread into 2.5 cm/ 1 in squares. Cut the Camembert into 2.5 cm/1 in cubes.

2 Heat 45 ml/3 tbsp of the oil in a frying pan. Add the bread and cook over a high heat for 5 minutes, stirring constantly, until golden all over. Reduce the heat, add the garlic and cook for 1 minute more. Remove the croûtons with a slotted spoon.

3 Tip the ratatouille into a pan and place over a medium heat, stirring occasionally, until hot.

4 Heat the remaining oil in the frying pan. Add the cheese cubes and sear over a high heat for 1 minute. Divide the hot ratatouille between two serving bowls, spoon the croûtons and cheese on top, garnish with the parsley and serve at once.

Ciabatta Rolls with Courgettes and Saffron

Split crunchy ciabatta rolls are filled with courgettes in a creamy tomato sauce flavoured with saffron. Use a mixture of green and yellow courgettes if possible.

Serves 4

INGREDIENTS
675 g/1½ lb small courgettes
15 ml/1 tbsp olive oil
2 shallots, freshly chopped
4 ciabatta rolls
200 g/7 oz can chopped tomatoes
pinch of sugar
a few saffron threads
50 ml/2 fl oz/¼ cup single cream
salt and freshly ground black pepper

courgettes

chopped tomatoes

saffron

shallots

ciabatta rolls   *single cream*

COOK'S TIP
To avoid heating your oven, heat the rolls in a microwave. Put them on a plate, cover with kitchen paper and heat on HIGH for 30–45 seconds.

1 Preheat the oven to 180°C/350°F/ Gas 4. Top and tail the courgettes. Then, using a sharp knife, cut them into 4 cm/1½ in lengths, then cut each piece into quarters lengthways.

2 Heat the oil in a large frying pan. Add the shallots and fry over a moderate heat for 1–2 minutes. Put the rolls into the oven to warm through.

3 Add the courgettes to the shallots, mix well and cook for 6 minutes, stirring frequently, until just beginning to soften.

4 Stir in the tomatoes and sugar. Steep the saffron threads in a little hot water for a few minutes, then add to the pan with the cream. Cook for 4 minutes, stirring occasionally. Season to taste. Split open the rolls and fill with the courgettes and sauce.

Cheese en Croûte with Tomato Sauce

Melt-in-the-mouth cheese sandwiches, pan-fried and served with a tomato sauce.

Serves 4

INGREDIENTS
50 g/2 oz/¹/₄ cup butter, softened
1 small onion, chopped
400 g/14 oz can chopped tomatoes
large thyme sprig
8 slices of white bread
115 g/4 oz mature Cheddar cheese
2 eggs
30 ml/2 tbsp milk
30 ml/2 tbsp groundnut oil
salt and freshly ground black pepper
8 cos lettuce leaves, to serve

thyme

eggs

chopped tomatoes

onion

milk

Cheddar cheese

butter

white bread

1 Melt 25 g/1 oz/2 tbsp of the butter in a frying pan. Add the onion and cook for 3–4 minutes until soft.

2 Stir in the chopped tomatoes. Strip the leaves from the thyme sprig and stir them into the pan. Add salt and pepper to taste, then cover the pan and cook for 5 minutes.

3 Meanwhile, spread the remaining butter over the slices of bread.

4 Slice the cheese thinly. Arrange on 4 slices of bread and sandwich with the remaining slices. Trim the crusts.

5 Beat the eggs and milk together in a bowl. Add salt and pepper to taste and pour into a shallow dish.

6 Heat the oil in a large frying pan. Dip each sandwich in the egg mixture until well-coated. Add to the hot oil and fry for 2 minutes on each side, until the coating is golden and the cheese has melted. Cut each sandwich into quarters. Arrange on individual plates garnished with the cos lettuce leaves. Serve the tomato sauce in a bowl to one side.

COOK'S TIP
If the tomato sauce is a little tart, add a pinch of sugar, or liven it up with a dash of Tabasco.

Potato, Broccoli and Red Pepper Stir-fry

A hot and hearty stir-fry of vegetables with just a hint of fresh ginger.

Serves 2

INGREDIENTS
450 g/1 lb potatoes
45 ml/3 tbsp groundnut oil
50 g/2 oz/¼ cup butter
1 small onion, chopped
1 red pepper, seeded and chopped
225 g/8 oz broccoli, broken
  into florets
2.5 cm/1 in piece of fresh root
  ginger, peeled and grated
salt and freshly ground black pepper

red pepper   *butter*

broccoli   *onion*

root ginger   *potatoes*

COOK'S TIP
Although a wok is the preferred pan for stir-frying, for this recipe a flat frying pan is best to cook the potatoes quickly.

1 Peel the potatoes and cut them into 1 cm/½ in dice.

2 Heat the oil in a large frying pan and add the potatoes. Cook for 8 minutes over a high heat, stirring and tossing occasionally, until the potatoes are browned and just tender.

3 Drain off the oil. Add the butter to the potatoes in the pan. As soon as it melts, add the onion and red pepper. Stir-fry for 2 minutes.

4 Add the broccoli florets and ginger to the pan. Stir-fry for 2–3 minutes more, taking care not to break up the potatoes. Add salt and pepper to taste and serve at once.

Bubble and Squeak with Fried Eggs

Next time you are serving mashed potato, make double the amount and chill half so that you can make this tasty dish the next day.

Serves 2

INGREDIENTS

¹/₂ Savoy cabbage
50 g/2 oz/¹/₄ cup butter
1 small onion, finely chopped
450 g/1 lb mashed potato
15 ml/1 tbsp chopped fresh parsley
15 ml/1 tbsp vegetable oil
2 eggs
salt and freshly ground black pepper
2 tomatoes, halved, to serve

eggs

mashed potato

butter

onion

Savoy cabbage

parsley

1 Cut out and discard the hard core of the cabbage. Strip off and discard the outer layer of leaves. Finely slice the remaining cabbage and set aside.

2 Melt the butter in a large frying pan. Add the onion and fry for 2–3 minutes until just tender. Reduce the heat slightly, add the cabbage and cook, stirring constantly, for 2–3 minutes.

3 Add the mashed potato to the pan. Stir to combine. Cook for 5–6 minutes until the mixture starts to brown. Stir in the chopped parsley and add salt and pepper to taste. Transfer the mixture to a serving dish and keep hot.

4 Wipe the pan clean. Heat the oil and fry the eggs until just set. Serve the bubble and squeak on individual plates, adding a fried egg and two tomato halves to each portion. Sprinkle with black pepper.

Potato, Spinach and Pine Nut Gratin

Pine nuts add a satisfying crunch to this gratin of wafer-thin potato slices and spinach in a creamy cheese sauce.

Serves 2

INGREDIENTS
450 g/1 lb potatoes
1 garlic clove, crushed
3 spring onions, thinly sliced
150 ml/¹/₄ pint/²/₃ cup single cream
250 ml/8 fl oz/1 cup milk
225 g/8 oz frozen chopped
  spinach, thawed
115 g/4 oz Cheddar cheese, grated
25 g/1 oz/¹/₄ cup pine nuts
salt and freshly ground black pepper

spinach

potatoes

garlic clove

pine nuts

spring onions

Cheddar cheese

single cream

1 Peel the potoates and cut them carefully into wafer-thin slices. Spread them out in a large, heavy-based, non-stick frying pan.

2 Scatter the crushed garlic and sliced spring onions evenly over the potatoes.

3 Pour the cream and milk over the potatoes. Place the pan over a gentle heat, cover and cook for 8 minutes or until the potatoes are tender.

4 Using both hands, squeeze the spinach dry. Add the spinach to the potatoes, mixing lightly. Cover the pan and cook for 2 minutes more.

5 Add salt and pepper to taste, then spoon the mixture into a gratin dish. Preheat the grill.

6 Sprinkle the grated cheese and pine nuts over the spinach mixture. Heat under the grill for 2–3 minutes until the topping is golden. A simple lettuce and tomato salad makes an excellent accompaniment to this dish.

Creamy Cannellini Beans with Asparagus

Cannellini beans in a creamy sauce contrast with tender asparagus in this tasty toast topper.

Serves 2

INGREDIENTS
10 ml/2 tsp butter
1 small onion, finely chopped
1 small carrot, grated
5 ml/1 tsp fresh thyme leaves
400 g/14 oz can cannellini
  beans, drained
150 ml/¼ pint/⅔ cup single cream
115 g/4 oz young asparagus
  spears, trimmed
2 slices of fresh cut Granary bread
salt and freshly ground black pepper

Granary bread *carrot* *thyme*

butter

asparagus spears

single cream

onion

cannellini beans

parsley

1 Melt the butter in a pan. Add the onion and carrot and fry over a moderate heat for 4 minutes until soft. Add the thyme leaves.

2 Rinse the cannellini beans under cold running water. Drain thoroughly, then add to the onion and carrot. Mix lightly.

3 Pour in the cream and heat slowly to just below boiling point, stirring occasionally. Remove the pan from the heat and add salt and pepper to taste. Preheat the grill.

4 Place the asparagus spears in a saucepan. Pour over just enough boiling water to cover. Poach for 3–4 minutes until the spears are just tender.

5 Meanwhile, toast the bread under the grill until both sides are golden.

6 Place the toast on individual plates. Drain the asparagus and divide the spears between the slices of toast. Spoon the bean mixture over each portion and serve.

COOK'S TIP
Use your favourite variety of canned beans such as borlotti, haricot or flageolets.

Red Fried Rice

This vibrant rice dish owes its appeal as much to the bright colours of red onion, red pepper and cherry tomatoes as it does to their distinctive flavours.

Serves 2

INGREDIENTS
115 g/4 oz/⅝ cup basmati rice
30 ml/2 tbsp groundnut oil
1 small red onion, chopped
1 red pepper, seeded and chopped
225 g/8 oz cherry tomatoes, halved
2 eggs, beaten
salt and freshly ground black pepper

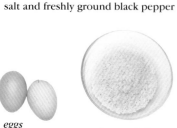

eggs

basmati rice

cherry tomatoes

red onion

red pepper

1 Wash the rice several times under cold running water. Drain well. Bring a large pan of water to the boil, add the rice and cook for 10–12 minutes.

2 Meanwhile, heat the oil in a wok until very hot. Add the onion and red pepper and stir-fry for 2–3 minutes. Add the cherry tomatoes and stir-fry for a further 2 minutes.

3 Pour in the beaten eggs all at once. Cook for 30 seconds without stirring, then stir to break up the egg as it sets.

4 Drain the cooked rice thoroughly, add to the wok and toss it over the heat with the vegetable and egg mixture for 3 minutes. Season the fried rice with salt and pepper to taste.

Chick-pea Stew

This hearty chick-pea and vegetable stew makes a filling meal. It is delicious served with garlic-flavoured mashed potato.

Serves 4

INGREDIENTS

30 ml/2 tbsp olive oil
1 small onion, chopped
225 g/8 oz carrots, halved
  and thinly sliced
2.5 ml/½ tsp ground cumin
5 ml/1 tsp ground coriander
30 ml/2 tbsp plain flour
225 g/8 oz courgettes, sliced
200 g/7 oz can sweetcorn, drained
400 g/14 oz can chick-peas, drained
30 ml/2 tbsp tomato purée
200 ml/7 fl oz/scant 1 cup hot
  vegetable stock
salt and freshly ground black pepper

onion *tomato purée*

sweetcorn *chick-peas*

stock cube

ground cumin

carrots

ground coriander

plain flour

courgettes

1 Heat the oil in a frying pan. Add the onion and carrots. Toss to coat the vegetables in the oil, then cook over moderate heat for 4 minutes.

2 Add the ground cumin, coriander and flour. Stir and cook for 1 minute.

COOK'S TIP

For speedy garlic-flavoured mashed potatoes simply mash potatoes with garlic butter and stir in chopped fresh parsley and a little crème fraîche.

3 Cut the courgette slices in half. Add them to the pan with the sweetcorn, chick-peas, tomato purée and vegetable stock. Stir well. Cook for 10 minutes, stirring frequently.

4 Taste the stew and add salt and pepper. Serve at once, with garlic-flavoured mashed potato (see Cook's Tip), if liked.

Aubergine Pilaff

This hearty dish is made with bulgur wheat and aubergine, flavoured with fresh mint.

Serves 2

INGREDIENTS
2 medium aubergines
60-90 ml/4-6 tbsp sunflower oil
1 small onion, finely chopped
175 g/6 oz/1 cup bulgur wheat
450 ml/16 fl oz/scant 2 cups
  vegetable stock
30 ml/2 tbsp pine nuts, toasted
15 ml/1 tbsp chopped fresh mint
salt and freshly ground black pepper

FOR THE GARNISH
lime wedges
lemon wedges
torn mint leaves

mint

pine nuts

onion

stock cube

bulgur wheat

aubergines

1 Trim the ends from the aubergines. Using a sharp knife, cut them into neat sticks and then into 1 cm/½ in dice.

2 Heat 60 ml/4 tbsp of the oil in a large frying pan. Add the onion and sauté for 1 minute.

COOK'S TIP

To cut down on the cooking time, soak the bulgur wheat in water to cover by 2.5 cm/1 in for up to 8 hours. Drain and continue as described in the recipe, reducing the cooking time to 8 minutes.

3 Add the diced aubergine. Cook over a high heat, stirring frequently, for about 4 minutes until just tender. Add the remaining oil if needed.

4 Stir in the bulgur wheat, mixing well, then pour in the vegetable stock. Bring to the boil, then lower the heat and simmer for 10 minutes or until all the liquid has evaporated. Season to taste.

5 Add the pine nuts, stir gently with a wooden spoon, then stir in the mint.

6 Spoon the pilaff on to individual plates and garnish each portion with lime and lemon wedges. Sprinkle with torn mint leaves for extra colour.

Houmus with Pan-fried Courgettes

Pan-fried courgettes are perfect for dipping into home-made houmus.

Serves 4

INGREDIENTS
225 g/8 oz can chick-peas
2 garlic cloves, roughly chopped
90 ml/6 tbsp lemon juice
60 ml/4 tbsp tahini paste
75 ml/5 tbsp olive oil, plus extra
  to serve
5 ml/1 tsp ground cumin
450 g/1 lb small courgettes
salt and freshly ground black pepper

TO SERVE
paprika
pitta bread
black olives

courgettes

chick-peas　　*lemon*

tahini paste

garlic cloves

ground cumin

1 Drain the chick-peas, reserving the liquid from the can, and tip them into a food processor or blender. Blend to a smooth purée, adding a small amount of the reserved liquid if necessary.

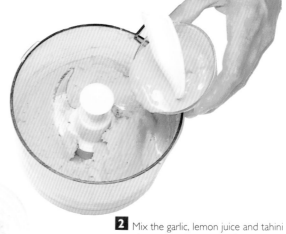

2 Mix the garlic, lemon juice and tahini together and add to the food processor or blender. Process until smooth. With the machine running, gradually add 45 ml/3 tbsp of the olive oil through the feeder tube or lid.

3 Add the cumin, with salt and pepper to taste. Process to mix, then scrape the houmus into a bowl. Cover and chill until required.

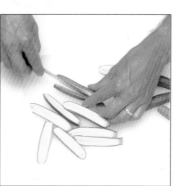

4 Top and tail the courgettes. Slice them lengthways into even-size pieces.

5 Heat the remaining oil in a large frying pan. Season the courgettes and fry them for 2–3 minutes on each side until just tender.

COOK'S TIP
Houmus is also delicious served with pan-fried or grilled aubergine slices.

6 Divide the courgettes among four individual plates. Spoon a portion of houmus on to each plate, sprinkle with paprika, add two or three pieces of sliced pitta bread and serve with olives.

Lentil Stir-fry

Mushrooms, artichokes, sugar snap peas and
lentils make a satisfying stir-fry supper.

Serves 2–3

INGREDIENTS
115 g/4 oz sugar snap peas
25 g/1 oz butter
1 small onion, chopped
115 g/4 oz cup or brown cap
  mushrooms, sliced
400 g/14 oz can artichoke hearts,
  drained and halved
400 g/14 oz can green
  lentils, drained
60 ml/4 tbsp single cream
25 g/1 oz/¼ cup flaked
  almonds, toasted
salt and freshly ground black pepper
French bread, to serve

single cream

green lentils

cup mushrooms

sugar snap peas

flaked almonds

artichoke hearts

onion

COOK'S TIP

Use Greek yogurt instead of the
cream, if preferred.

1 Bring a pan of salted water to the
boil, add the sugar snap peas and cook
for about 4 minutes until just tender.
Drain, refresh under cold running water,
then drain again. Pat dry the peas with
kitchen paper and set aside.

2 Melt the butter in a frying pan.
Cook the chopped onion for 2–3
minutes, stirring occasionally.

3 Add the sliced mushrooms to the
onion. Stir until combined, then cook for
2–3 minutes until just tender. Add the
artichokes, sugar snap peas and lentils to
the pan. Stir-fry for 2 minutes.

4 Stir in the cream and almonds and
cook for 1 minute. Season to taste. Serve
at once, with chunks of French bread.

Nut Pilaff with Omelette Rolls

A wonderful mixture of textures – soft fluffy rice with crunchy nuts and omelette rolls.

Serves 2

INGREDIENTS
175 g/6 oz/1 cup basmati rice
15 ml/1 tbsp sunflower oil
1 small onion, chopped
1 red pepper, finely diced
350 ml/12 fl oz/1½ cups hot
  vegetable stock
2 eggs
25 g/1 oz/¼ cup salted peanuts
15 ml/1 tbsp soy sauce
salt and freshly ground black pepper
parsley sprigs, to garnish

salted
peanuts

parsley

onion

stock cube

eggs

basmati rice

red pepper

soy sauce

1 Wash the rice several times under cold running water. Drain thoroughly. Heat half the oil in a large frying pan. Fry the onion and pepper for 2–3 minutes then stir in the rice and stock. Bring to the boil and cook for 10 minutes until the rice is tender.

2 Meanwhile, beat the eggs lightly with salt and pepper to taste. Heat the remaining oil in a second large frying pan. Pour in the eggs and tilt the pan to cover the base thinly. Cook the omelette for 1 minute, then flip it over and cook the other side for 1 minute.

3 Slide the omelette on to a clean board and roll it up tightly. Cut the omelette roll into 8 slices.

4 Stir the peanuts and the soy sauce into the pilaff and add black pepper to taste. Turn the pilaff into a serving dish, arrange the omelette rolls on top and garnish with the parsley. Serve at once.

Kedgeree with French Beans and Mushrooms

Crunchy French beans and mushrooms are the star ingredients in this vegetarian version of an old favourite.

Serves 2

INGREDIENTS

115 g/4 oz/⁵/₄ cup basmati rice
3 eggs
175 g/6 oz French beans, trimmed
50 g/2 oz/¹/₄ cup butter
1 onion, finely chopped
225 g/8 oz brown cap mushrooms, quartered
30 ml/2 tbsp single cream
15 ml/1 tbsp chopped fresh parsley
salt and freshly ground black pepper

single cream

brown cap mushrooms

parsley

onion

butter

French beans

eggs

basmati rice

1 Wash the rice several times under cold running water. Drain thoroughly. Bring a pan of water to the boil, add the rice and cook for 10–12 minutes until tender. Drain thoroughly.

2 Half fill a second pan with water, add the eggs and bring to the boil. Lower the heat and simmer for 8 minutes. Drain the eggs, cool them under cold water, then remove the shells.

3 Bring another pan of water to the boil and cook the French beans for 5 minutes. Drain, refresh under cold running water, then drain again.

4 Melt the butter in a large frying pan. Add the onion and mushrooms. Cook for 2–3 minutes over a moderate heat.

5 Add the French beans and rice to the onion mixture. Stir lightly to mix. Cook for 2 minutes. Cut the hard-boiled eggs in wedges and add them to the pan.

6 Stir in the cream and parsley, taking care not to break up the eggs. Reheat the kedgeree, but do not allow it to boil. Serve at once.

Chick-pea Falafel with Coriander Dip

Little balls of spicy chick-pea purée, deep-fried until crisp, are served together with a coriander-flavoured mayonnaise.

Serves 4

INGREDIENTS
400 g/14 oz can chick-peas, drained
6 spring onions, finely sliced
1 egg
2.5 ml/¹⁄₂ tsp ground turmeric
1 garlic clove, crushed
5 ml/1 tsp ground cumin
60 ml/4 tbsp chopped
  fresh coriander
oil for deep-frying
1 small red chilli, seeded and
  finely chopped
45 ml/3 tbsp mayonnaise
salt and freshly ground black pepper
coriander sprig, to garnish

coriander

spring onions

chick-peas

ground turmeric

ground cumin

egg

garlic clove

red chilli

mayonnaise

COOK'S TIP
If you have time, chill the chick-pea purée before making it into balls. It will be easier to shape.

1 Tip the chick-peas into a food processor or blender. Add the spring onions and process to a smooth purée. Add the egg, turmeric, garlic, cumin and 15 ml/1 tbsp of the chopped coriander. Process briefly to mix, then add salt and pepper to taste.

2 Working with clean wet hands, shape the chick-pea mixture into about 16 small balls.

3 Heat the oil for deep-frying to 180°C/350°F or until a cube of bread, when added to the oil, browns in 30–45 seconds. Deep-fry the falafel in batches for 2–3 minutes or until golden. Drain on kitchen paper, then place in a serving bowl.

4 Stir the remaining coriander and the chilli into the mayonnaise. Garnish with the coriander sprig and serve alongside the falafel.

Three Bean Salad with Yogurt Dressing

This tangy bean and pasta salad is great on its own or can be served as a side dish.

Serves 3–4

INGREDIENTS
75 g/3 oz penne or other dried
  pasta shapes
2 tomatoes
200 g/7 oz can red kidney
  beans, drained
200 g/7 oz can cannellini
  beans, drained
200 g/7 oz can chick-peas, drained
1 green pepper, seeded and diced
75 ml/3 tbsp natural yogurt
30 ml/2 tbsp sunflower oil
grated rind of ¹/₂ lemon
10 ml/2 tsp wholegrain mustard
5 ml/1 tsp chopped fresh oregano
salt and freshly ground black pepper

penne

oregano

green
pepper

red kidney
beans

cannellini
beans

natural
yogurt

chick-peas

lemon

wholegrain
mustard

tomatoes

1 Bring a large pan of salted water to the boil. Add the pasta and cook for 10–12 minutes until just tender. Drain, cool under cold water and drain again.

2 Make a cross with the tip of a sharp knife in each of the tomatoes. Plunge them into a bowl of boiling water for 30 seconds. Remove with a slotted spoon or spatula, run under cold water and peel away the skins. Cut the tomatoes into segments.

3 Drain the canned beans and chick-peas in a colander, rinse them under cold water and drain again. Tip into a bowl. Add the tomato segments, green pepper and pasta.

4 Whisk the yogurt until smooth. Gradually whisk in the oil, lemon rind and mustard. Stir in the oregano and salt and pepper to taste. Pour the dressing over the salad and toss well.

INDEX